LETTERS
FROM A
MARTYRED
CHRISTIAN

LETTERS
FROM A
MARTYRED
CHRISTIAN

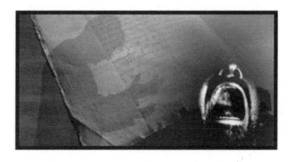

In AD 67, Aulus Aurelius and his family were
murdered for their faith. These are his letters to you.

H.L. HUSSMANN

Casebound - ISBN 978-0-9779286-5-1
Softcover - ISBN 978-0-9779286-6-8
Ebook(mobi) - ISBN 0-9779286-7-5
Ebook(epub) - ISBN 0-9779286-8-3
All scripture quotations, unless otherwise indicated, are
taken from the HOLY BIBLE, NEW INTERNATIONAL
VERSION®. NIV®. Copyright © 1973, 1978, 1984 by
International Bible Society. Used by permission of
Zondervan. All rights reserved.

Quote on page 101 from Harold Lindsell.

The story of Vietnamese Christian Hien Pham from chapter
eight is based on true events: "Hien Pham: A Man Set
Apart," by Ravi Zacharias, *A Slice of Infinity*, No. 762,
originally printed 8 November 2004 (www.rzim.org) Used
by permission of Ravi Zacharias International Ministries.

Requests for information should be addressed to
*PBL Productions, 1505 Doran Road, Suite 101
Murray, KY 42071*
Cover and Interior Design by: PBL Productions
Design Consultant: Ryan L. Brooks
Cover Photo: Jennie Short

To schedule H.L. Hussmann to speak at your church,
conference, or ministry, see HLHussmann.com:

From Amazon Reviews:

"... at once provocative, challenging, and emotionally wrenching."

"I didn't care what projects I was letting go - I just wanted to keep reading."

"*Letters From a Martyred Christian* will compel you to reevaluate your own life in action, thought, or belief."

"I literally could not put it down. The stories drew me in, and I couldn't wait to read more."

"As I turned the last page of the book, I found myself a little sad. Aulus was quickly becoming an old friend."

"*Letters From A Martyred Christian* will stick in my mind for a long time to come."

"I don't typically recommend books, but I find myself constantly spreading the word about how much *Letters From a Martyred Christian* draws you in."

"When reading this book you will find yourself crying at some points and having to stop and ... worship God at others."

"I lead a small group of college students each week, and we encourage each other to share our faith on a regular basis. I plan to use the book as a guide to keep focus on what is important."

"I just couldn't put it down. My wife called me several times to come to bed, and I just couldn't pull myself away. I read the entire book that night in one sitting."

"I only seek to read books that have the potential to change one's life, and this is a book that could do that!"

"This book of letters seems as personal as letters from a long-lost friend; someone you haven't heard from in a while & someone you can't wait to hear from again."

"Definitely one of my all-time favorites."

"I couldn't stop. I will now start reading the book again because I don't want to miss anything."

"How many of us are willing to go that far for Christ?"

"It was an engaging, thought-provoking, and enjoyable read that challenged my perspectives with each letter."

"An intriguing look at life after death [and] what really matters in the end. This book will make you think."

"Each letter pulls you closer in and leaves you wanting to know God more intimately than ever."

"I enjoyed the concept of this book. It is something different and different is a virtue in the world of books. I suppose [it] could be called an anti-*Screwtape Letters*. *The Screwtape Letters* are written from Hell's view but this book looks down from Heaven."

Table of Contents

Acknowledgments

I am extremely grateful to Assemblies of God U.S. Missions for providing this version of LFMC to the attendees of The World Missions Summit 3. My thanks go out in particular to Zollie L. Smith, Jr., for his friendship and faithful service to the Kingdom of God. We are extremely blessed to have you as a leader. Thanks also to Ramona Edgman and Libby Wiseman for your excellence and hard work on this project.

In addition, thanks so much to E. Scott and Crystal Martin for going to bat to help make this happen. I've appreciated your encouragement more than you could know. I pray, as I know you do, that the end result will be hundreds of students inspired to surrender all to Jesus.

And finally, as always, thanks to my dear friends Becky Lile and Ryan Brooks for their help in "beautifying" the final product. You guys are fantastic.

Foreword

As you hold this book in your hands, I trust that you are finding your time at The World Missions Summit to be one that challenges and inspires you to step into the role God has for you. H. L. Hussmann, one of our Chi Alpha campus missionaries, has written a fiction story, but the experiences of the martyred character are the everyday experiences of believers across the globe who suffer at the hands of injustice and persecution, even to the point of death.

Following Christ has a cost. It means we no longer live for ourselves; we live and serve at the pleasure of our King. While in America we do not do so at the risk of our lives as some do in other countries, we still need to live with a sense of urgency! Christ will return, and before He comes, we must do all we can to rescue the lost and ensure that none perish.

Maybe you are attending this conference, and for the first time you are considering what it means for you to live out and share your faith. Maybe you are here because you already have made a commitment to answer a call to ministry and missions, and you are seeking direction. Maybe this is all new to you, but I assure you that God wants to use this time to speak to you. As you consider giving a year and praying about a lifetime, it is my prayer that this book will challenge you not only to count the cost of a life devoted to serving God's kingdom, but to strengthen your resolve to see His Kingdom advance here on earth.

U.S. Missions just celebrated its 75th anniversary, and I am overwhelmed with gratefulness to God for His faithfulness to us over all that time. But it is the next 25 years that really excite me. I am eager with anticipation for you and your generation to step in alongside me and my fellow missionaries in these next years. Already, young people are changing the face of U.S. Missions, helping us reach new people groups we didn't realize we had been missing. The opportunities are boundless!

May God richly bless you as you seek His face and His will for your life. I look forward to working in the harvest field with you in the years to come.

That none perish,

Zollie L. Smith, Jr.
Executive Director
Assemblies of God U.S. Missions

In *Letters From A Martyred Christian*, H.L. Hussmann has adroitly researched history and antiquity as well as brought to life pragmatic applications on living the gospel and dying to self in today's culture. The characters will challenge you, and throughout the book you will be compelled to evaluate your life and commitment to Jesus. I as well as my family have been deeply touched by his work and the perspective it brings to our daily living.

The book had me thinking about Rome, and I have always wanted to take my wife Crystal there. I had found the city fascinating, filled with history, antiquity and uniqueness, and it had become one of my top five global destinations. We had the opportunity this past April to spend three days in this majestic city. One afternoon, while on our tour bus, we stopped at the portentous Circus Maximus, the tour guide explaining that this was the exact place of the great chariot races, but even more significant, this was where the early Christians were martyred, torn apart by lions. She went on to explain that the Colosseum was really not used for the Christian martyrs as it was too small, only holding between 50,000 and 60,000 people, whereas the Circus Maximus held up to 250,000 people.

As we heard the stories and overlooked the antiquity, Crystal and I began to openly contemplate what we would have done had we been one of those early Christians who met their fate with the lions. Could we have gone through with it? Just how far are we really willing to go for this Jesus we claim to love and serve? It was a true gut check as the memories from reading *Letters From A Martyred Christian* were coming to life again.

Later during the summer, while serving a brief time back home in Kyrgyzstan, I was hearing the Islamic call to prayer while a team of Chi Alphans from U. C. Davis were running a sports camp for the kids of the city; they were touching the inconvenient lost far away from their home. They set some amenities aside, saved and raised some money, and adjusted their will to come there. They were willing to go a long way for Jesus' sake, and I recall thinking to myself, "I bet they could do 'it'."

You will enjoy The World Missions Summit 3 edition of *Letters From A Martyred Christian*, a gift to you from U. S. Missions, and while reading the book you will discover what the 'it' is.

E. Scott Martin
Student Mission Director
Chi Alpha U. S. A.

Preface

I love the character Aulus Aurelius.

As I have tried to think like him, I have been challenged and convicted. Pure Christianity—giving oneself to God and sacrificing everything for others—isn't easy. But we need more voices pushing us toward a radical faith in Jesus reflected in every area of our lives. Aulus is such a voice.

The stories are fiction with a small amount of non-fiction, but even the latter has received "creative liberties." Any particular eschatological views implied were tools toward interesting fiction. Please treat this book as a collection of parables with no intention of asserting literal truth about Heaven and the afterlife. It is thought-provoking fiction and nothing more.

I encourage you to read each of these letters one at a time and think about them before you move on. You will be best served reading *LFMC* over time rather than all at once.

Each chapter was designed to make you think, but more so, to stir you to action. Beginning on page 147, you will find discussion questions and steps of action you can use as an individual or in a group setting. For multiple copies for your Sunday school class or small group, see page 165.

May you, like Aulus, give everything to Jesus.

"Living Dead is not a novel idea. The gospel has always included suffering, and, when God's people live and die with joy, Jesus is glorified and draws all peoples to Himself. H.L. Hussmann's overview of those who have lived and died for Jesus reminds us that we are but the latest generation of those called to follow Him all the way to the cross. I have read it and been moved by it to deeper, simpler consecration."

Dick Brogden - Editor of the *Live Dead Journal*

LETTER ONE
The Story of Aulus Aurelius

Dear Friend,

Let me tell you about the day I died.

I watched my wife tortured and killed. I saw my seven-year-old daughter murdered. And, worst of all, I heard my thirteen-year-old son denounce Christ. Then, with my neighbors forced to watch, they killed me.

My name is Aulus Aurelius, though some of my friends added Pius Agricola (the pious farmer). You may call me Aulus.

I raised crops in a province south of Rome and converted to Christianity in the year 54. I pastored a group of believers who met in my home, and for several years we enjoyed peace as our crops flourished, our community expanded, and, most important, our fellowship grew. Nearly every soul in our province heard the Gospel, and a great many responded. Every family within ten miles of my home received a personal testimony of the Lord Jesus. I saw to it myself.

For three years, we had been haunted by the fact that Christians around the country were being persecuted. Since the fires of Rome in 64, the government had done its best to stifle the spread of the Gospel. Great numbers were dragged from their homes and fed to the lions. Others were killed in "battle" in arenas throughout the countryside. Still others were nailed to trees and skinned alive. Some were sawed in two, and some were dragged to death behind horses. Many were burned at the stake to illuminate the gardens of Emperor Nero.

Many nights I was unable to sleep. I would pace in our garden, staring at the stars and pleading with God. I had three requests: One, that I would remain faithful to the Gospel. Two, that if need be, I would die in a way that pleased Him. And three, that my wife and children would not suffer. Two of my requests were granted.

The day I died was an idyllic autumn day in the year 67.

I was returning home from a two-day journey selling crops. The streets of my town were empty. The stores were closed. Faces peered at me through shop windows but then vanished inside. My friend, Markus Valerius, a local storeowner, stepped outside and glanced around the area.

"Aulus. Come here." He didn't leave the porch and beckoned with one hand. "Hurry up. Come on. Come on."

I led my horse in his direction. "Markus, what's happening here? Where is everyone?"

He jumped down the stairs and placed his hand on my shoulder, pulling me in the direction of his shop. "We'll talk inside."

I tied off my cart and entered the building. He closed and latched the door, then produced a pair of chairs and motioned for me to sit, though neither of us did.

"I need to tell you something, Aulus." He clasped his hands together in front of his mouth and paced, staring at the floor.

His soft leather shoes scraped the wooden planks as he walked. I could feel my heartbeat increase as I waited, knowing what was happening but hoping for another explanation. The pulse of blood in my ears soon matched his steps four to one. He tried to speak, but the words didn't come. I couldn't wait any longer.

"When did they arrive?"

Markus stopped pacing but kept his eyes on the floor. "I ... I mean, they ...."

"The Romans, Markus—when did they get here?"

His shoulders slumped, and he shook his head. "This afternoon. There were more than twenty—all on horses. We didn't want to tell them anything, but what choice did we have? They were asking about you. They went to your home, Aulus. That was almost an hour ago."

Visions of my family flashed through my head as my stomach tightened. I gripped the chair in front of me as my legs threatened to give out.

When steadied, I slid the chair aside and took a weak step toward the door. "I need to go, Markus. Take care of my cart. If anything should happen, use it for the Kingdom."

Stepping in front of me, Markus placed his hand on my chest. "Aulus, I can't let you do that. If you stay here with me, or even go away for a while, maybe everything will .... Listen, I have supplies. You could—"

"Markus, you know I have to go," I said. "Every moment I stay could be the last I might have with my family." I wanted to push him aside, but I knew that would never do. I had been the one who introduced Markus to Jesus, and over the years he had become like a brother to me. I needed to move with haste, but I also needed to say goodbye. I embraced him as he wept.

"We all knew this day was coming, Markus. We just didn't know when. I have to go. No matter what you hear, don't be afraid." Taking him by the shoulders, I looked into his eyes. "Keep the faith, Markus. That's all that matters. Do you understand?" He nodded, sniffing. I placed my hands on the sides of his head and kissed him on the cheek, holding his head against

H.L. HUSSMANN

mine. "I love you, my brother. I believe in you. Everything will be as it should."

With that, I reached for the door.

My mind was whirling. When I arrived, would my wife and children be alive? Would the Romans torture me or kill me outright? If tortured, could I withstand? I prayed as I unlatched my cart and mounted my horse.

Make me strong. Make me strong. Make me strong.

The few minutes it took to get home seemed like hours as my thoughts turned to the past—my wedding day, the births of my children, and countless meals shared with friends and family. And behind my thoughts was a gnawing terror that made me want to scream and cry or dismount and vomit.

When I arrived, my nightmares were realized. A crowd of my neighbors had been herded by two dozen soldiers. Three of the armored men were still on horses, but the others were moving around the farm on foot. My house had been ransacked. My wife and children were on their knees in the yard, hands tied behind their backs.

"That's him! That's the one!"

Everyone turned as I slid from my saddle.

"That's him! That's him!"

As two soldiers moved toward me, I recognized the man speaking and berated myself for my foolishness. Two weeks earlier I had met him in the market of a nearby village. Our stalls had been adjacent, and over the course of the day he had come to know much about me—and especially about my faith in Christ. I had tried to judge his character and felt I could trust him, so I invited him to come to our village and hear more about Jesus. I had felt uneasy about sharing with him, but it soon passed, as it always did. There was always the danger of meeting a Roman informant, but it was a risk we often took. In hundreds of situations before I had been safe. This man was the exception.

"Bring him to me!" One man commanded the soldiers. He had been standing over my wife when I arrived. At his order, the two men shoved me forward.

As they bound my hands and drove me to my knees, I looked at my wife.

"Maria, did they hurt you?" A swollen red mark across her cheek gave the answer.

"Silence!" I never knew which soldier said it, or which one hit me, but pain shot through the back of my head as something cracked against my skull. I pitched forward onto the ground. White lights spun through my vision. Coughing dirt from my mouth and struggling to stay conscious, I heard gasps and cries from my friends.

"You will speak only when the Optio tells you to speak, traitor!" The soldier grabbed my tunic and pulled me to a kneeling position. Dizziness and nausea swept over me, but I was strengthened at the sight of my wife. My children were crying, but she was not. Her brown eyes showed no fear as she looked at me.

I'm so glad you made it.

It was unspoken, but clear.

The Optio turned toward my gathered friends and read from a wax tablet, his booming voice traveling across the acres of fields surrounding my home. "Let it be known throughout this province and all of Rome that membership in, and propagation of, the cult of Christus is a treasonous offense, punishable by death." Then, lowering the tablet, "It has been made clear that one Aulus Aurelius is guilty of such treason, as is his family."

Strutting in front of my wife and children, he continued. "Aulus Aurelius, you are convicted of treason against your Emperor. It is well known you are a member of this cult and teach its vile doctrines. You have been denounced by this man and by your neighbors."

He walked closer to me and spoke in softer tones, though loud enough for all present to hear. "However, as you may know, your Emperor is generous and kind-hearted and has given many the opportunity to repent of such foolishness." He spun again toward the crowd and stood in place, feet together. "Let it also be known that, if abandoned, membership in this cult is a forgivable offense. The Emperor has no desire to punish his subjects for crimes of ignorance."

"Aulus Aurelius, today you have the chance to save yourself. Denounce this false god Christus and worship the gods of Rome, and you and your family will be spared. Fail to do this, and you will die here today."

With dirt caked on my face and sweat rolling down my cheeks, I remembered Jesus. He was silent before His accusers. My thinking, though foggy, was to do the same. I said nothing. Instead, I looked at the faces of my wife and two beautiful children and did my best to comfort them. Several seconds ticked by with only the shuffling sound of horses and the sobbing of my children to be heard. My son refused to look at me.

"I don't have time for this!" the Optio said, hastening toward my children. Without breaking stride, he grabbed my daughter Evie by her tunic and jerked her into the air. Her legs flailed as he dragged her across the yard. She tried to scream, but the garment against her throat allowed only coughing and gasping. Several of my neighbors stepped forward, but a soldier slammed the butt of his spear into one man's stomach, sending him to his knees. Several guards moved in and raised their weapons.

Hoisting my daughter in the air, he slammed her into a water trough kept for the horses. She spasmed and twisted as she tried to escape. My wife was screaming, "No! Please, no!" My son was trying to scoot closer to his mother. "Mama ... mama ... do something!"

My body began to shake. "Please, she is just a girl. Take me! Let her go!" I tried to move toward my daughter, but on my knees it was hopeless.

One of the soldiers grabbed me by the shoulder and pulled me back. I would have done anything to save her, including breaking that soldier's neck, but my hands were locked. I could feel the ropes burning into my flesh as I pulled against them.

And between sobs, "Jesus! Oh, Jesus! Help me! Jesus! Jesus!"

"Renounce Him, traitor! This is your last warning!" Pulling Evie's head out of the trough just enough so she could gasp for air, the Optio yelled, "I will not ask again!"

I was reduced in a moment from a father and a pastor to an animal. Base instincts rose up as I fought and screamed into the air.

There is no describing my helplessness as she coughed water from her lungs and cried. Her face showed incomprehension and terror as her eyes darted around the area. Between her wails, one word escaped, slammed into my chest, and ripped me apart from the inside out.

"Daddy!"

For the shortest moment I considered anything. A weakness descended upon me, and everything I held dear turned to darkness.

No need to be strong.

No need to set the example anymore.

Do what it takes to save my girl.

Anything.

But that is when it happened.

Behind four of the soldiers I saw Him. I couldn't make out His form, and it still seems like a dream, but I am certain I saw His face. He smiled at me as He moved among the men. I'm not sure how it happened, and when I have asked Him about it since He has only laughed, but on that day Jesus came, and everything changed.

The next few minutes seem like a story I heard elsewhere. The Optio was yelling. I am not sure what he was saying, but his thin eyes were fixed on me. He wanted my resistance. He was enjoying this. He was sick. Perverted. Demonic. And I loved him. It still seems impossible, but it is true. He was killing my daughter, and all I could think was, "Father, set him free." If I wasn't certain before, I now knew: Jesus was with me.

After drowning my daughter and throwing her body on the ground, he turned toward my son, now face down and begging. It took a moment to understand what he was shouting. "I renounce Jesus! I renounce Jesus! I am not a Christian! I am not a Christian!" It was as if he were trying to bury his face in the ground as he writhed in the dirt, pleading for his life. A part of me wanted to yell at him and tell him to remain strong. But another part, full of God's presence, knew even this would end well. I was experiencing the "peace which surpasses understanding."

H.L. HUSSMANN

The Optio nodded to a nearby soldier. "Release the boy." As he approached my wife, he addressed the crowd. "You see! The Emperor is gracious. Reject this treason and you will live."

He grabbed my wonderful Maria by the hair, pulled her to her feet and exposed her throat, turning her head sideways. He placed his blade over her neck and insisted, "Renounce Christus!" He was addressing Maria but looking at me.

"Renounce Christus and save your wife!" he said as he pressed his face against Maria's cheek, yelling next to her ear. He spat the name Christus as if cursing.

He didn't wait for a response and began to use his sword on Maria, stabbing her in the arms, shoulders, and hips. With each blow he yelled. "Christus! Christus! Christus! Where is He now?" His lips curled as he glared at me, eyes mocking. Maria was screaming and crumpled to the ground. She ground her teeth in pain.

Then I discovered that she, too, was aware of His presence. From the ground, she struggled to roll onto her back, blood soaking the earth below. She spoke, and her words filled me with joy. She was looking past her oppressor when she said the same simple phrase three times.

"Thank You."

"Thank You."

"Thank You."

Her chest was moving up and down as she sucked in breath. A single tear rolled down her cheek, and I noticed one soldier glance at me then look away.

Just before the Optio killed her with the heel of his boot, Maria focused on him and spoke her last. "He will forgive you if you ask."

My face was wet with tears as I watched her die, but in that moment—a moment wicked beyond imagination—I found the greatest strength I had ever known. I knew I would be with her soon, and her suffering was over. She had finished well. Her conviction gave me power, and I stood. I am not sure why I was allowed to do so. Whether the guard was stunned by my wife's words, or the Lord worked a miracle, didn't matter. I stood to my feet without reprisal. I turned to my neighbors and walked toward them, raising my voice. The power of the Holy Spirit filled me.

"WHO WILL STAND FOR JESUS?"

I looked from face to face. Time had slowed down. The soldiers were not moving. My neighbors stood helpless. Some looked back, and others averted their eyes. One woman, a close friend of my wife, was hysterical. She had collapsed to her knees and was wailing.

I asked again.

"WHO WILL STAND FOR JESUS?"

No answer came.

"WHO?"

Out of the corner of my eye I saw movement from the Optio. He was advancing toward me—slowly at first, but with increasing speed.

With my last seconds on Earth, I looked behind me, scanning the yard for my son. The Optio was coming closer. I heard his feet scraping the ground, and it seemed like he was growling.

My son was still on his knees. His bonds had been cut, but his hands were on the ground. His skin had turned pale, and his eyes were vacant as he stared at his mother's body. I could tell he was in shock. I raised my voice to get his attention.

"Son!"

There was no response. I said it again, louder.

"My son!"

I heard the Optio's rushing intake of breath as he charged. I could see him at the edge of my vision as he drew back his sword. He was still yelling something indiscernible. My son, somehow, slowly, turned away from his mother. At the last possible moment his eyes met mine. They were bloodshot and filled with pain. I spoke my last words.

"Never forget."

And then I heard clapping.

Applause.

Somewhere behind me was an uproar of cheering. I turned toward the sound.

I never saw the crowd. They were overshadowed by the One. I saw only Him, and He wore a broad smile and clapped His hands as

He spoke. "Yes! Yes! Yes! Aulus!" At once I was standing on a mountaintop, breathing the freshest of air, hearing the most beautiful melody ever composed. Health and youth flowed through my veins. Imagine the greatest joy you have ever experienced and multiply it a thousand, a million times, and you still could not know what I felt when He said my name.

"Well done, my friend! Well done!" He clasped His hands together as He approached. I tried to speak, but there were no words.

"Shhhhhhh," He said. He embraced me and then, placing His hand on my back, turned me around. There was mischief in His eyes.

"Watch what I do."

I was staring down the mountain and moving through the clouds. I was flying and, with a rush, caught up with the earth below. Looking down at my lifeless body, I saw my head had been severed. The Optio was standing over my remains, wiping the blood from his blade. Shaking his head in disgust, he moved toward his horse. The soldiers began to follow suit, but out of the silence, one of my neighbors spoke.

"I will stand."

The Optio jerked his head around, trying to find the perpetrator. The soldiers near the group raised their spears again, looking to the Optio for instructions. The crowd parted around the culprit.

Walking forward, the Optio extended his blade, holding it inches from the man's face.

"What did you say?"

My friend spoke again, enunciating every word.

"I said," and he stuck out his chin, exposing his throat to the sword, "I—will—stand!"

Somewhere nearby I heard more applause, and something beautiful rippled through the crowd below. Like a wave, from front to back, courage flowed. My neighbors couldn't see it as I did, but there was a glow as it filled them one by one.

Another spoke. "I, too, will stand."

My next door neighbor stepped forward. "I will stand for Jesus!"

And another. "I will stand for Jesus."

"I will stand."

My wife's friend, still crying, stood to her feet and yelled through broken sobs, "I will stand for Jesus! I will stand for Jesus!" A pause, and then, shouting at the top of her lungs, "JESUS!"

The rest of the crowd responded, and the name of Jesus rang out. "Jesus!" "Jesus!" They were all crying now. "Jesus!" Several raised their hands with eyes toward heaven as they worshipped. "Jesus!" "Jesus!" "Jesus!"

The Optio remained still, eyes narrowed and looking from face to face. The first man was glaring back, arms crossed. Lowering the blade, he shook his head again and let out a sigh. He had seen this before. He turned toward his horse and placed his sword in its sheath. He nodded toward the nearest soldier.

"Kill them all."

I didn't see what happened next. I only know that, without exception, every one of them died that day.

My son was the only survivor, but over the next few months, hundreds of people heard about what happened. I watched as, that night, deep in the woods behind my home, his face to the ground, my son repented. Unknown to him, angels surrounded him and prayed, filling him with strength, cleansing him from condemnation, and bringing forgiveness. I marveled as God changed him from a cowering boy into a powerful young man. Fourteen years later he died in the Colosseum, raising his hands in triumph and encouraging other believers to give their lives. My son's testimony did more for the Gospel than I had done in all my years as a believer. And today he is with me.

In almost two thousand years, I have seen tyrants strive to destroy the Gospel. I have watched hypocrites and blasphemers slander the Name. But I also have watched generations of Christians follow in our footsteps and lay down their lives. Many died physically, but others died in different ways. I have seen preachers brave city streets. I have watched people take in strangers. I have seen merchants sell everything and take their families to dangerous countries. I have seen

H.L. HUSSMANN

beautiful story after beautiful story as people lay down their lives for the sake of the Gospel, and I want to challenge you to die, too.

I have been granted permission to write these letters. I have observed the Church through history and can help you if you will listen. But I should make two points.

First, I will not use the kind of language you may expect. I understand modern culture. I have studied for hundreds of years and am fluent in more than three dozen languages. I am capable of expression in language you can understand.

Second, I am not God, nor do I know the full mind of God. I no longer see Him as through a glass dimly, but this only gives me a clearer view of His mystery. He is infinite, and having a hundred thousand lifetimes to know Him will only scratch the surface. The letters I write, though permitted by God, are not Scripture, nor should they hold Scripture's weight.

You also should understand there are topics that are forbidden. In your time on Earth, much will be kept a mystery. It is part of the wonder and release of Heaven to gain knowledge. What I share will be a small but valuable portion.

I pray you will find joy and motivation.

Your friend and mentor,

Aulus Aurelius

H.L. HUSSMANN

LETTER TWO
A Journey to Real Life

Dear Child of God,

Use your imagination and take a journey. The journey is long, but that is precisely the point.

You are looking at yourself from overhead, ten or twenty feet, and you are backing away at a slow pace. Imagine the view. What do you see looking down at thirty feet? At forty? At fifty? How far can you see on the horizon? Please, take a moment to imagine.

You float upward—a hundred feet, then two hundred, three hundred, four hundred. At five hundred feet, the curvature of the Earth becomes apparent. Roads disappear in the distance with scattered towns dotting the landscape.

You are accelerating now. One thousand, two thousand ... ten thousand feet. You see the Earth in its fullness, a perfect globe, spinning a lazy circle. Billions of people go on with their lives.

You are moving faster, and the Earth is shrinking away. Five miles, ten miles, a hundred miles. There is no sense of panic as you move through space. A shockwave shakes you and reverberates into the darkness as you eclipse the speed of sound.

The moon is approaching. Even at this speed it takes days for a toenail sliver of light to slide into a glowing orb as you pass to the side of the sun. Craters and canyons are evident as you sail by, faster and faster—two times, three times, four times the speed of sound.

For three days the sun consumes the horizon in an expanding ring as you speed toward the center. Still hundreds of miles away, the sheer blazing wall engulfs the limits of your vision. Up, down, left, and right you see nothing but an ocean of flame. Ignitions of gas and fire tentacle into space for thousands of miles. The hissing, rushing, and crashing deafen you.

How do we not hear this on Earth?

Faster than any jet, you skim the sun for days. Two weeks linger with nothing but raging flames and massive explosions. On the eighth day your trajectory shifts. Pulling away from the surface, the blackness of space returns—a thin line of darkness expands in tiny increments as the hours pass. Two days later you are away. You have reached the other side of the sun.

H.L. HUSSMANN

You accelerate again. A thousand times faster, ten thousand, a hundred thousand, two hundred thousand. The sun contracts in your vision. Hours later it is a speck among millions.

Five hundred thousand, eight hundred thousand ... a million times faster—faster than light. Four years later you've passed the nearest star. Smaller than the sun, it comes and goes in a red-orange burst of light.

Two million, six million, ten million times faster. Months pass between stars—searing white pinpoints and lumbering orange juggernauts.

Faster.

Faster.

Billions of stars zoom by like a photo shoot: *pop, pop, flash, pop.*

Solar systems rush away. Galaxies whirl around you and are gone. Darkness grips you, but a stronger force steals you away.

You travel for hundreds of millions of years.

And then whiteness blinds you.

It takes several minutes for your eyes to adjust.

You find yourself in an open courtyard. The floor is iridescent white marble and extends a thousand feet in all directions, forming a perfect circle. Beyond the marble edge you see emerald green grass and people milling about. There are four white columns the size of redwood trees. The weather is perfect.

The only other person in the courtyard approaches. A twenty-something, he's wearing blue jeans and a t-shirt with socks but no shoes. He is humming and scratches the back of his head when he looks at you.

"It's not as big as we thought, is it?"

"I'm sorry?"

He motions behind you with a nod. "Check it out, my friend."

Behind you is a simple pedestal, three feet high and carved of the same material as the floor. The top is bowl-shaped, and a jet black ball rotates as it hovers in the curve. The ball is eighteen inches across, and as you move closer you see countless tiny lights inside. Hands on your knees, you lean in, trying to take it in. Your head swims as you realize what you are seeing.

Padded steps approach from behind, and you feel a hand on your arm. "Don't worry. It freaks everyone out at first."

On closer inspection, your host may not be as young as you thought. His black hair glimmers, half way over his ears, and his dark brown eyes flash as he smiles, extending his hand.

"I'm Tian Wei."

You offer your hand, which he clasps. He pulls you in, wraps his arms around you, and squeezes.

"It's great to see you," he says.

He is beaming as he steps back and maintains a firm grip on your hand. It's clear he is from another country, but his language is so much like your own that you wonder if he was adopted. When you have the thought he laughs.

"We can talk about my heritage later, friend, but you've got a lot to learn. Come on. I've got something to show you."

You look back at the globe, and Tian Wei gives you a moment to stare. He still hasn't let go of your hand, and it makes you uncomfortable. Placing his other hand over yours, he says, "You'll get over that soon enough. Are you ready?"

"Where are we going?"

"Sightseeing."

As the words leave his mouth, you feel a rush in your stomach as both of you rise into the air. Your legs scramble for footing, and you grab Tian Wei's arm with your empty hand.

"You'll get used to that, too," he says. "Relax. Have faith."

After several seconds of swaying from one side to the other, you find your bearings and are able to let go with one hand and remain upright. Rising fifty feet, you observe the area nearby.

Hundreds of people are in the grass near the courtyard. Many are playing games or eating meals on blankets, but the location seems more a marketplace than a park. Others move among the stalls, peeling vegetables, and grinding spices.

"Wonderful, isn't it?"

"I don't understand. What am I looking at? Are those people working?"

Tian Wei grins. "You could call it that if you want, but where joy is a commodity it's not the best description."

He reads your blank stare and continues. "While joy is free and abundant here, the joy of individuals is unique and theirs to distribute. It's a limitless supply, but it is rare and precious, too. So yes, they are working. And yes, they are playing. But that's not what I wanted to show you."

You continue to climb, and the grass beyond the courtyard becomes a geometric work of art, perfectly manicured to join with other courtyards and buildings nearby. The combination forms a mosaic of color that pulls at every part of you. Every garden, fountain, and architectural wonder beckons you to approach, and you know you could spend years exploring the area below.

Tian Wei seems content not to speak as the ground shrinks away. After what must be ten thousand feet, you stop.

"This should do," he says.

You gaze in all directions, and again your mind spins. The courtyard area is a dot on a landscape that goes on as far as you can see. Too high to discern every structure, somehow you still know you are viewing museums, art galleries, centers of science and learning, and orchestral music halls. There are mansions, parks, and schools, and there are lakes, mountains, and prairies.

"We eat, work, study, and rest here. And, of course, worship." Tian Wei says. "In many ways it's not unlike where you come from, though each of those words means something different here."

"It's ... I don't know. It's ... amazing."

Removing his socks, Tian Wei says, "That's the best you can do?" He drops the socks, which fall toward the courtyard and, unless your eyes are failing, vanish in the air. He lets go of your hand and spins in a circle with his arms held outward. "It's better than amazing, friend. It's ... crystal."

You wonder at floating alone and consider spinning, but dismiss the thought.

"Crystal?" you say.

"It's the best I could do with your vocabulary. It's flawless ... transparent—unlike your hesitance to dance." He tucks his arms in at his side and spins faster. While he rotates he speaks. "Look down. Do you see the place you came from?"

You peer below and try to make out the orb on the pedestal. You squint but can't even see the mammoth pillars nearby.

"No, I can't. It's too small and too far away."

He slows to a halt and looks at you with expectation.

"And ...?"

"And ... what?"

"That's the point. Do you not understand?"

You stare at your feet, which are also bare, and you wonder how they got that way.

"No, I'm sorry, I don't."

"The point is, that place is nothing. It is, as you said, 'too small and too far away.' You will be shocked at how soon its memory fades."

While he is speaking, the light surrounding you dims. Tian Wei becomes a blur as he spins again.

The horizon rushes toward you as the ground pulls you in, straight into the courtyard and back into the sphere.

In seconds your journey is reversed—too fast to take it in. There is a rushing sound flashing lights, explosions, and icy air whips your face.

In an instant you find yourself back where you began, reading this letter. And you hear Tian Wei's voice one last time.

"Remember what you saw, friend. *This* world is everything. That world is not."

I began with this journey for a reason. If my letters benefit you in any way, I pray you will see this: the world you are in is not your home. It will be remembered as a brief stop along the way, like one deep breath before the first pace of a marathon—overlooked and nearly forgotten.

Many hold on to that breath. They scrape and claw and refuse to let go. Don't be one of them. True life is letting go of life.

I know from your perspective the world is all-consuming. The time seems real and long-lasting. The opinions of others shape you. Material things seem comfortable and secure. But they are a flash, too brief to invest in. All will be made new. All will be born again.

H.L. HUSSMANN

Paul wrote to the church in Colossae, "Set your mind on things above, not on earthly things." There may be no greater wisdom.

The next time you are tempted or discouraged, think about this journey. Go outside. Stare at the sky. And realize that the place you sleep, the clothes on your body, and the opinions of men will amount to nothing. Only what is done for Christ will last. Present yourself to Him and hold nothing back.

Surrendered,

Aulus

H.L. HUSSMANN

LETTER THREE
A Shared Trait of Heaven

Beloved,

One of my favorite activities is to sit at the gates of Heaven and watch people enter.

Black people, white people, and people of every color between come through. People who died young and people who died at an old age enter every day. There is a constant flow of former doctors, lawyers, and engineers joined by people who never came near a school or hospital. I have seen people speaking Arabic, people speaking Mandarin, and people speaking for the first time as they entered. Former priests and former prostitutes come inside.

People become transparent, in a way, when they come here. At times I can see their history. I can see their prior joys and pains. I can see a shadow of their choices, whether wicked or righteous. We wear a portion of our history like clothing that radiates the glory of Jesus. Much is laid bare. There is no way to completely hide who you have been, nor would you want to. The shameful parts of your life on Earth become a badge of transformation in Heaven, bringing glory to God and illustrating His mercy.

As I watched today, I saw a businessman who had made millions. He was soon followed by a man who had lived in his car. In the same line of people was a woman raised in Calcutta. She had died of AIDS after early years of selling her body for food. Behind her were three teens who died together in a car wreck.

There were people from all over the world: Canada, Afghanistan, Belize, Puerto Rico, Uganda, and North Korea. They were people with differing political and social views. Some had been intelligent and beautiful. Others had never heard a compliment. From spiritual expression to family life they were diverse. But they all had one characteristic in common.

I remember a day when I was reminded of this. It was years ago. Like today, I was watching people file into Heaven. I was smiling, laughing, and introducing myself. My friend Emir approached and sat down. "I thought I'd find you here," he said.

An outbreak of dancing had occurred in the square in front of us, and people who had never met before were swinging one another around. I glanced at my friend. "You know how much I love it here."

"I do indeed, Aulus, but today I have come to ask you an important question." He grinned, and light bounced off a gold tooth he had chosen to keep. A baker by hobby, Emir's clothing filled the air with the smell of fresh-baked bread—an aroma that matched the warmth of his personality. His smile was infectious, and the Lord had used him many times to teach me.

"What's that?"

"The question is this," he said, and waved a hand in front of the crowd. "What is the same about all these people?"

My first thought was the most obvious—Jesus had saved them—but I knew my friend was looking for something else. I had learned long ago to think before responding.

In a line of people like that, every person has a different story and faced different temptations on Earth. One man's life had been controlled by doubt. Another woman had blamed God for her son's death. An Irish man from Killarney had beaten other men. A married Russian woman had five lovers. An Indonesian man had been bored.

The line into Heaven can stretch for miles, and every person has a past—abuser, blasphemer, liar, purposefully ignorant, uncaring, or hateful. My new answer was barely less obvious than the first.

"Um, none of us deserves to be here?" I said.

Emir laughed aloud and slapped me on the shoulder. "Of course, Aulus, you knew that already! But what else? Look closely."

I turned again and prayed for insight.

"I'll give you a hint. Who *don't* you see?"

There were former murderers, swindlers, and even child molesters in line that day, but it didn't take long to see who wasn't there. There was no one who entered with head held high, trusting his own worth. There was no one entering because she had been an "honest seeker" or had maintained her "intellectual integrity," although these things often lead to the humility needed. No one entered relying on a religious family, theological degrees, or donations to charity. When I had watched Heaven's processional before, I had seen no exceptions. I had never seen a self-righteous person cross the threshold. The line of people entering Heaven is always a line of broken people. But more, it's a line of broken people who know they are broken. They have no delusions of qualifying on their own. Self-righteous before? Yes, all of them at one time. But self-righteous on entry? Never.

"None of us deserves to be here, and ... we all know it."

Emir stood to his feet, smiling and clapping his hands. "Yes, yes, but what else, my friend? What else?" As he asked the question he joined in the dancing, linking arms with a young girl from Nepal and spinning around. As he danced his way into the crowd he turned back and yelled again. "You're getting it, Aulus! Now, what else?" Soon, his thick dark hair vanished in the throng.

As people danced and sang, embracing loved ones they hadn't seen in years, parts of the crowd moved down side roads, exploring with friends new and old. Others remained. Some continued dancing. One fired off questions, trying to unravel Heaven's mysteries in his first moments here.

One older gentleman caught my attention as he stood with hands on his head. He was weeping as he turned a slow circle, and I could see him mouthing something. I watched him for a few moments, and as I focused my attention, even a hundred yards away, I could make out his words. They were whispered in my ear. "Yes. Yes. Yes! Thank You! Thank You! Thank You!"

This man had been faithful to God for decades. He had touched more lives than most who come here. He had loved and served many. But he knew he arrived, not because of his own goodness, and not because of years of service, but because of the mercy of God. That unassuming nature was what had driven him. It was humility that had made him great.

Please listen carefully, friend. Self-confidence, apart from God, is the road to Hell. Humility is part of the key to Heaven, and pride locks people outside the gates. The Kingdom of God is the "Great Reverse." The weak become strong. The poor become rich. The hungry are filled. And the last become first. Jesus said many times, "God exalts the humble but brings low the proud."

God's goodness is the only goodness, and it is available to us as water is to a cup. But the cup must be cleaned, and it cannot clean itself. Even humility cannot be achieved through human effort. It must be received.

As you will see in another letter, there was one choice in the beginning: God or self. Every person has chosen self and walked toward destruction. But the question has been rephrased through the cross of Christ.

"Keep yourself, or come back to Me?"

Without humility, the rest of my writings will be worthless to you. It is the key to growth and learning. Are you humble, my friend?

Pray these words: "I don't deserve You. I cannot make my own way. Teach me. Show me. I am Your servant." No matter how far you have walked toward God, the next step requires the same as the first—humility.

When Jesus died, the barrier of pride between God and man crashed down. A bridge was created between Heaven and Earth. But it is a bridge impossible to navigate when blinded by self-dependence. It requires the vision of the One who sees clearly—Jesus Christ, the Messiah of God. We cannot cross the bridge alone.

H.L. HUSSMANN

Every person either will enter Heaven with humility, where the last shreds of self-sufficiency are destroyed, or will implode into the fire of self without God.

Now, let me tell you the rest of the story.

The older man was still thanking God when music filled the square. I had seen this many times, and it always ended with a celebration. As the music intensified, the crowd spread out, making room for the man in the center. As is common here, the people in the area were knit together in heart and mind and knew to honor him. They backed away and bowed in respect. As they split down the middle they created a path down the main street of the City, and a pulse of joy swept through us all. He was being promoted, and we watched as he was transformed.

His physical form didn't change—not in a way I could describe to you. But the difference between the man who now stood before us and the man who was there moments before was the difference between a servant and a king. Imagine someone standing up straighter, pushing his shoulders back, and holding his head higher, and you can begin to picture what happened. It was a thrill to be nearby. He was covered in pride, but not the pride I mentioned before—not selfish pride. This was a pure and wonderful sort of pride that gives confidence, security, and a greater desire to serve. Great rest comes only after hard labor, and this kind of confidence comes at the end of a lifetime of sacrifice. While everyone in Heaven is a celebrity (that is, "one to be celebrated"), this man was special, and God honored him.

He walked down the road through the parted crowd. The music faded, and the people were hushed in this moment of reverence. I knew where he was going. I once had been invited in a similar way. He would be taken to a place created only for him—a place of intimacy with God. He would be given a name that only he and Jesus would know. He would be showered with knowledge, blessings, and joy and placed in a position of authority. He had sacrificed for decades, but his rewards would last forever.

A day is coming when all men will receive what is due, and humility is the foundation of eternal rewards.

I pray you will be amazed at the reception you receive here.

Aulus

LETTER FOUR
Choosing to Choose

Dear Friend,

It was a day that would set the course of human history. Every beating, rape, and cancer cell would come as a result.

Uncharacteristic fog filled the woods, and the sun fought to penetrate the trees, alternating rays of light and beams of shadow. Two young inhabitants padded through the grass, gathering food from the trees and plants. Reaching the center of the Garden, they stopped a hundred yards from a particular Tree.

The woman removed her basket from its perch on her head. As she filled it with roots she glanced at the Tree's towering branches. The fruit was different from anything else.

"Smells good, doesn't it?" she said.

"Don't even think about it," the man replied as he topped off his own reed basket. "You know what He said."

The woman looked to her work and tried not to care. "I know. It just seems odd. That's all."

She could feel the man looking at her, but he was silent. Was he listening, or would he correct her again?

For several moments, the birds sang in the trees nearby. An animal moved through the bushes, and the woman cleaned her day's collection, gently rubbing the roots. The rich soil fell in piles with little effort.

He finally spoke. "Forget it. He has His reasons."

She continued her task and nodded. "True, but maybe it's some kind of test."

Adam placed his basket on the ground, sat with his legs crossed, and grabbed an apple. "I don't know how much clearer it could be, Eve. 'You will surely die' sounds pretty bad to me. If nothing else, why bother? We've got it good here." He crunched a big bite and half-smiled with a cheek full of fruit. He patted the ground next to him. "Come here and sit with me," he said, raising his eyebrows twice. The woman laughed and moved toward him. "You, my dear, have a one-track mind."

"I won't deny it," he said, taking her hand. "Have I told you how beautiful you look today?"

"She's right, you know."

H.L. HUSSMANN

The voice came from behind. The woman snapped her head around, sucked in her breath and covered her mouth, looking into the woods. The man stood and placed himself between the woman and the sound. Thirty feet away, from between the trees, a dragon emerged on all fours. Eight feet from nose to tail and three feet off the ground, the slender creature half crawled, half slithered toward them, bowing its head.

"Forgive me, friends. I had no intention of startling you," it said, moving from four legs to two, standing four feet higher. Its elongated snout flared as it swayed from side to side. Its tail coiled, providing balance for its silver-scaled body.

The man reached behind him and touched his wife, maintaining his position.

"Who–?"

"A messenger. I couldn't help overhearing. I'm here to assist."

The woman placed a hand on the man's shoulder and looked the dragon over.

"A messenger? From whom? ... From Him?"

The snake bowed again, lower. His forked tongue flicked between words. "Is there ... anyone else, my lady?" From his lowered position his eyes rose to meet hers. He didn't wait for an answer and fell forward to all fours. He sped past the wide-eyed pair and toward the great Tree.

"Follow me, friends."

Adam looked at Eve and shrugged his shoulders. The two turned and watched the beast scurry away.

Adam placed one hand in the crook of Eve's back, and the other on her naked hip, whispering in her ear. "Let's see what he has to say." She looked up at him, grinned, and they gave chase.

Jogging to catch up, Eve yelled ahead. "Did you say I was right about something?"

The creature kept moving but called back. "All will be made clear."

The two caught up with the serpent as he passed under the lower branches. The trunk of the Tree was still eighty yards away, and it had taken Adam 150 paces to walk around it when they had measured it before. At the center, the lowest branches were dozens of feet overhead. The thick limbs bowed under their own weight and came close enough for a person to touch on the outer perimeter. A blanket of brown and green formed a canopy above the grass. Glistening in sweat from the run, the two passed into the shade and the cool air beneath.

The dragon was back on two legs and sniffing the fruit seven feet off the ground.

"Gorgeous, isn't it?"

The man stood with hands on his hips, catching his breath. "You were saying something to my wife?"

The creature plucked the largest piece of fruit he could reach. Holding it in one hand, he pierced it with two bony fingers and with a twist snapped it in half. Clear juices sprayed into the air and flowed down his arms as he extended a piece to each of them. When they refused he dropped the fruit on the ground and licked the fluids away with a guttural sigh that rattled in his throat like a growl. "Hmmmmm. There's nothing like it."

The two looked at each other and then down at the fruit. The dragon seemed not to care. He was walking, looking from branch to branch and sniffing the air.

The man took a step backward. "We can't eat these." Eve had closed her eyes and was taking a deep breath. A pungent sweetness hung in the air.

The creature found what he was looking for. He reached into the tree and removed a piece, which he threw into his mouth, chewed twice, and swallowed. He turned his head and looked at them. "Of course, friend ... but then, it is *your* choice, is it not?"

Eve opened her eyes. "What do you mean?"

Adam pulled Eve back a step, placed his mouth against her ear, and whispered so only she could hear. "Remember what He said, Eve. Eating that is risking death."

The dragon plopped to the ground and snaked his way back to them. Sitting on his rear haunches, he crossed his arms and cocked his head to the side, peering at them through ebony eyes. "Did He really say that?"

Eve gasped. Adam looked the beast over and folded his arms as well. "Did He say what?"

"That you would die?"

"How did you–?"

"It doesn't matter. Are you sure that's what He said ... exactly?" He looked at the woman. "Did He? Did He say that?"

Eve stared at the monster and then at the ground, shifting her weight from one foot to the other. "Yes ... I mean, well, He said something like that. I wasn't actually there." She reached to take Adam's arm. "But I believe my husband."

The dragon scratched his chin and looked into the branches. "Of course, it doesn't matter the exact words He used, does it? Sometimes He says one thing but means another. Doesn't He?"

Adam's eyes narrowed. "Does He?"

The creature shrugged. "Of course. You won't actually die. Not like you think. Death? Yes, but not physical death. That would be ridiculous. He didn't create you just to kill you. Surely you know He's better than that."

The pair stared at him.

"You *will* surely die if you eat it, friends. You will die to tyranny, control, and ownership. You will die to dependence on another. The Lord knows these things are evil, and that is why He has given you this test."

Adam thought for a moment.

"So ... it *is* a test?"

"A test of your will, friend, a test of your will." And with a huff, "Or lack thereof, I might say." He moved much closer now and stood in front of the two, looking down into their faces.

"You must decide who will be in control: Him or you?"

Eve shook her head. "I don't understand. How can we–?"

The dragon looked at the fruit lying at their feet. "Pick it up. It's the best in the Garden. Why would He keep it from you? It will be your choice when you eat, not His. Your eyes will be opened. You won't need Him to tell you what you can't do. *You* will decide. You will know good from evil and will choose, just like Him. Won't that be nice? Don't you think He would want that?"

Eve squatted to look at the fruit. "He said not to even touch it."

"But did He mean it? That is the question. Surely you can see I touched it, and I am fine. I chose to touch it because I can. The decision was mine, like it is yours. You can be free like me."

Adam squatted next to Eve with his elbows on his knees. He laced his hands in front of his mouth and shook his head. "I'm ... not sure."

Eve said to Adam, "We don't have to decide now. We could talk to Him about it ... see what He says."

The dragon snorted and lowered himself to their level. "But that would ruin the test, now wouldn't it? Even if He says to eat, the test is failed. He is still in control."

The monster looked at Eve. "The fruit is nothing, my lady. The decision, though ...."

Eve nodded her head and squeezed Adam's arm. "It does look delicious. He's always said He wants what's best."

The man ran his hands back and forth through his hair several times and stared at the ground. Eve failed to notice the silence that hung in the air. The trees were vacant and the bushes empty. The dragon walked away.

And standing, Adam made his decision.

"Go ahead, give it a try."

And, in doing so, they chose for all men.

The death they experienced that day wasn't physical. It was more "real" than that. Spiritual reality supersedes the physical. Their spirits died that day. God's Spirit is life, and He was evicted. They denied Him rightful place as King. He refuses to inhabit what He does not own.

But the full consequences took time.

Before they had "chosen to choose" they had known what it was to walk in God's presence, to be intimate with Him, and to share in His thoughts. He ruled their lives. They existed in a pure relationship with their Creator and an unpolluted relationship with each other—the reasons for which they were created.

But when they chose independence over dependence, they walked a path that cannot sustain life in any area—spirit, mind, or body. When their spirits died, their minds, in a way, followed. And later, their bodies would pass as well. God was not equivocating when He said, "You will surely die." But death is a process.

This death has trickled through the ages. Every father passes it to his sons and every mother to her daughters. Everyone chooses to choose. Everyone wants control. And, as a result, everyone is dying—dying on Earth and, without a miracle, dying forever. But praise God that through Christ Jesus that miracle came.

Today, the enemy's goal is similar to what it was in the beginning. He desires that no one would return to God. And he is good at what he does. He is the ultimate con man—offering something tasty, something shiny, in exchange for souls. And his question to you is always the same:

"Who is in charge here?"

My prayer is that you will see his game for what it is and refuse to be tempted. I will explain more in my next letter.

"Freedom" is often bondage in disguise.

Aulus

H.L. HUSSMANN

LETTER FIVE
The Beauty That Destroys

Beloved One,

I want to illustrate how the enemy works.

Years ago, Kate Jeffries sat near the Applied Computing Building at the University of Dundee in Dundee, Scotland.

It was a rare spring day when the rain held off and the sun peeked from behind the clouds. Students lounged in groups, sharing picnics, while others threw Frisbees or kicked soccer balls on the manicured grass of the campus green. Kate and her friends, Ali and Jocelyn, shared coffee and sandwiches.

Kate was a true-born Scot, but her Irish red hair and bright green eyes betrayed her heritage from the other island. She had freckled, ruddy skin and several extra pounds in all the wrong places. She was crunching a baguette and talking with her mouth full.

"So in physics today, my professor drew a picture of a stick-man pushing a box across what he called a 'frictionless surface,'" Kate said, and laughed. "Can you believe that?"

She looked to the other girls, who kept eating but glanced at each other and back at Kate.

"Uhm, ... yeah, so?" Jocelyn said.

Kate rolled her eyes. "Don't you get it? If the surface was frictionless, how could the little guy walk on it?" Slapping Ali on the knee, she said, "He'd fall flat on his face!"

The two girls looked at each other again and broke into laughter. Jocelyn covered her mouth to keep from spitting out her coffee, and Ali shook her head.

"So I raised my hand and told the professor just that. And guess what he did."

Ali continued to shake her head and stare. "Kate, I have ... no idea." Jocelyn was busy looking for a napkin.

"He drew a rocket pack on the little guy's back!" Kate laughed again and pumped her fist. "Yes! Score one for the professor!" At this, all three girls had a good laugh—Kate at her story and the other two at Kate. As the laughter died down, she began to speak again, but a British accent interrupted from nearby.

"Could you do that again?"

A tall and skinny Brit approached. He wore several layers, though the weather was warm. His pale skin was more blemished than Kate's, and strands of hair peeked from under his cap. His eyes were nice, and they locked on to the redhead.

All three girls stared, but Jocelyn spoke. "Could we do *what* exactly again?"

He looked down and shuffled his feet. His hands were in his pockets. "Well, it's kind of embarrassing, I guess," he said. He glanced at Kate but then back at the ground. "But would you mind smiling like that again?"

Ali and Jocelyn giggled, and Ali elbowed Kate in the arm. Kate could feel her cheeks flush as she shifted in her seat.

"Oh, hey, listen ... I didn't mean to embarrass you," he said, pulling off his hat and twisting it between his hands. His thick black hair was mashed on one side while a cow lick on the other tried to flee his head.

He shifted the cap from hand to hand. "I just ... well, look ... I was just having a lousy day, of sorts. You know, lots going wrong and all. And when I saw you smiling and laughing ... well ... it was, uhm—" He hesitated but then looked her square in the eyes again. "Well, it was helpful. And if you don't mind, I'd like you to do it again."

None of the girls could help but smile now. As Kate grinned she heard Jocelyn whisper under her breath, "That's soooo sweet."

The young man watched Kate grin for a few moments and smiled in return. He then closed his eyes, placed his hands and his hat over his heart, and drew in a deep breath with an audible "ahhhh" as it released.

"Perfect."

A moment later he opened his eyes and extended his hand. "By the way, I'm Michael."

Six months later Kate came back from an abortion alone.

He said he couldn't get off work, but he promised to meet her at the apartment with Chinese takeout and as much time as she needed to talk. She was already crying when she unlocked the door, but what she found inside made her grip the door frame to steady herself.

Her apartment was trashed.

Every drawer in the kitchen had been pulled out and the contents dumped. The refrigerator had been overturned. Milk and juice were pooled on the tile floor and ran along the foyer wall. Her furniture was shredded and her stereo speakers kicked in. There were holes in some of the walls, and a layer of dust filled the air, floating through the light from a nearby window.

Half stepping, half stumbling, she moved back into the hall and reached for her phone. As she dialed, she noticed some papers hanging on the wall, just inside the door.

The documents were secured with a knife from the kitchen, and at the top of the stack was a picture—Michael and Kate resting together on a campus bench. Her head was in his lap, and both of them were laughing. The photo had been taken three weeks after they met.

The papers were statements from her bank. They showed wire transfers made that day, draining both her personal checking account of €1200 and the savings account inherited from her grandfather: €96,000 intended for her education and a down payment on her first home.

Written in marker across the back of the second page were words that for years would make her want to die.

"Did you really think I could love you?"

The police would inform her he had conned another girl in Dundee at the same time for a lesser amount. He was a suspect in several other jobs throughout Europe—a professional who skipped from country to country. The odds of finding him were slim. He preyed on girls with rich families and often held his charade for months before revealing himself. He had left more than a dozen girls bankrupt and crushed.

Let me explain how Kate's story relates to the enemy of your soul, for there is much to learn.

First, understand that his methods never change. The specifics vary from person to person, but the strategy is constant. He mimics what is beautiful by disguising something ugly. He substitutes pride for confidence, codependence for intimacy, and lust for love. He offers the kingdom of this world for the Kingdom of God. He makes the hideous seem attractive and the vacant seem full. Kate believed she had found love, and many fall for a similar con.

Second, realize that every person is a target of his bankruptcy.

God made you as a vessel that overflows with what is beautiful. Because of this, you are a target. Be careful. Every part of you that is empty of God is filled with the "nothing" that describes this world. Without God-filled confidence you are vulnerable to pride. Being filled with His Spirit brings intimacy, and being barren of the same breeds codependence. God is love, and lust fills the void of His absence. You will be filled either with Everything or with nothing. The only way to discern the difference is to know Him.

One day this world will say, "Did you really think I could love you?"

Do not be taken in.

Aulus

LETTER SIX
The Heart of the Matter

My Friend,

I must convey another sad tale to show you
what matters to God.

Sharri Anne Fouri was startled awake when her
father's '71 Corolla slammed into a pothole.
Muddy water shot from under the tire and
sprayed the dirt road between her hometown of
DeAar, South Africa, and whatever destination
her dad had in mind. She was eight years old, and
they had been driving for hours.

Running her fingers through her tight-curled
black hair, she found dust from the road had
formed a layer while she slept. The tiny hairs on
one side of her face tingled as she pulled away

from the window and rubbed her cheek with a water bottle for relief.

Her father Simeon gripped both sides of the steering wheel and stared ahead. The ebony skin on his jaw line flexed again and again as he ground his rear teeth—a habit Sharri had noticed the last few weeks.

She didn't expect an answer, but she had to try. Even with her legs crossed, the pain in her abdomen was growing. She leaned forward and whispered, a mouse disturbing a giant.

"Papa?"

She waited. The car continued its up and down rhythm as her father tried to navigate the smoothest parts of the road.

She tried again. "Papa? Please don't be mad, but I need to *go.*"

Her father's right hand slid an inch down the steering wheel, and his chest moved up and down with a single deep breath.

Sharri sat back in her seat and leaned against the window. She knew better than to press him, especially not today. She couldn't understand his recent behavior, but his urgency that morning had left her frightened and confused.

They accelerated past a moped carrying a family of four: a man and a woman with a toddler and an infant pressed between them. The lady on the back smiled and waved at Sharri, wiggling her fingers. The young girls in her lap were sound asleep. Sharri smiled back and fought the lump that formed in her throat as the family vanished in the dust behind the car.

It had been six months since her mother died.

It had begun with a small brown spot on the woman's left ankle. Similar purple and brown blotches soon covered her feet, crawled up her legs, and worked their way down her arms. Sharri's parents had tried to conceal it, but she had overheard them several times. It was "the disease," and no one they knew had ever survived.

For the last three months of her life, her mother had stayed in bed, and Sharri had spent as much time with her as possible. She had done her best to help around the house. She learned to collect and boil water, and she swept the floor every day. But most of her time was spent in bed with her mom, where they talked for hours. Her mother would embrace her while Sharri rubbed her tiny hands across the ugly tumors.

"Under that spot is skin that loves you," was always her mother's response when she saw the concern in Sharri's eyes. The little girl would wiggle in closer and listen to her mother's breathing.

As the condition worsened, speech became impossible, but the days of lying together continued. Her father had left Sharri alone, lying in the bed, for almost an hour after the cadence of breath came to its final beat. She had pulled her mother's arms tighter and cried in silence, her lips pressed against weathered hands.

"Sharri Anne ..."

Sharri snapped back to the present and realized the car had stopped. They had turned down a side road and parked. High strands of corn formed a hallway that vanished in the distance, and the buzzing moped soon passed by. The only other sounds were the car engine and the rattle of the stalks in the breeze.

Simeon turned off the key and reached through his window to open the door from the outside. He shoved the door open with his shoulder. His feet crunched in the gravel as he walked behind the car and came to the back passenger side door where Sharri sat. Her almond eyes squinted at her father's silhouette as he closed the gap between her and the sun.

His eyes left hers and stared up the road as he reached for the handle.

"This is a good spot," he said. Sharri noticed as he ran his other hand over his dark, bald head that his fingers were shaking. She paused and looked around at the fields.

"Get out of the car, girl!" he said, making her jump. She scrambled out as the tightness in her belly intensified.

Her father slammed the door behind her. He reached through the front window and pulled out her small gray and red knapsack. The gray had once been white, but years of use had transformed it. Her mother had sewn on several patches that now barely held it together.

"Take this." Her father shoved the bag into her stomach and let go. She grabbed it with both arms before it could fall. "You'll need it. There's paper inside." He pointed into the stalks of corn. "Go there. Do your business."

Sharri noticed when he pointed that his hand was trembling even more. His eyes were bloodshot, and moisture formed in the curves.

"But ... father—"

"WHAT DID I SAY, *MA CHÉRIE*?!" It was a variation of her name she hadn't heard in months, but it never had been yelled at her. It had been reserved for tender moments. Her father's face was turning red. Two smooth drops now overflowed his eyelids and journeyed down his cheeks. He pointed again. "GO!"

Sharri dropped the sack and pushed toward her father, grabbing him by the pant leg.

"Papa! Please! I'm sorry, I don't need to go," she said. "Let's go. Can we go? Please, papa? I can wait."

Her father leaned his head back and yelled at the sky—an angry, shrieking growl that he turned toward her.

"WHAT IS WRONG WITH YOU?!" His eyes were wild, and he was weeping. She let go of his pants and took a step away. Warm liquid flowed down her legs and pooled in her boots.

"WHY CAN'T YOU JUST DO AS I SAY, GIRL?!" He grabbed her by the shoulder and spun her around, pushing her toward the rows of corn. "Get in there!" He grabbed her sack and threw it over her head and into the field. He had never laid a hand on her before, and Sharri didn't know what to do. She ran sobbing into the wall of green. The stalks whipped her in the arms and face as she ran as fast as she could from the car.

Fifty feet in, she stopped and fell to the ground, wrapping her arms around her knees. She rocked back and forth and cried as she listened to the tires spin in the dirt and peel away.

She would be found by a farmer three days later, lying in the road and unconscious from dehydration. She would be in shock for weeks after she was revived. Years later she would discover that on the same day her father had abandoned her he had driven his car into a river. His body was found downstream.

⁂

I tell you this because I hope it disturbs you. It's a story that strikes to the deepest nerve, and I can attest it breaks the heart of God. Hers is a story of anguish and suffering that can only come from one source—a broken relationship.

There are many pains on Earth and many sources of suffering, but this kind is the most terrible. If you envision a man on his knees, pounding the ground with his fists and screaming at the sky through wet eyes, "NO, NO, NO!" you assume his loss has been relational. A spouse has been unfaithful. A friend has betrayed. A son has died.

In human language, there are no worse words:

Lonely
Betrayed
Abandoned
Neglected
Belittled
Molested
Despised
Abused
Ignored

Each is a word of pain, and all come from broken relationships.

From the beginning, man was created in relationship. When God said, "Let *us* make man in *our* image," the relational aspect of the Creator was sewn into the one created. The essence of God was planted in man, and the God who has always been is the God who is Three in One. God is, at His core, a relationship. He is love.

When Jesus walked the Earth, His message was clear: two commandments were preeminent. Love God. Love others. The message of Jesus was one of relationship.

At the center of your life is the need for connection. First, you need connection with God—a vibrant, life-giving dance where He takes the lead and you follow. In my next letter I'll talk about pursuing this.

Second, when you experience that love, He changes you to become a vessel that the joy, peace, and hope of the Master flows through. As you dance with Him, you take the hands of other people and help them dance along. Everything He has done and everything He will ever do is centered on this.

When God revealed Himself to man, He could have chosen many titles—Commander, Master, Supreme Power—and while He is all of these, He has revealed Himself first as Father. He made Himself known as One who is close.

Now, let me show you what He does.

I wish I could tell you the next sixteen years were easy for Sharri Anne, but it would not be true. She was passed from foster home to foster home until, at fourteen, after three years of abuse, she ran away. At seventeen she returned to foster care. After leaving the system at eighteen, she worked at a filling station and rented a filthy studio apartment. Most months she could keep the utilities on.

It was the eve of her twenty-fourth birthday when she gave up. She was a month and a half behind on her rent but spent money at a local hardware store anyway. She purchased clear

H.L. HUSSMANN

plastic sheeting and returned home, where she carefully lined the basin of her bathtub and taped down the edges of the plastic. She poked a half-dollar-sized hole above the drain and pushed a plug into the opening.

A few minutes later she sat at her kitchen table and stared at the paper in her hands. She rocked back and forth on a chair that had one leg shorter than the others.

Dear officers,
Please send someone to Apartment 3A at 1800 Minaar Street. There's a key under the mat. I'm sorry for the mess. Sharri

She had thrown a bottle of cheap vodka in her purse after leaving work and swigged shots as she read the letter several times, trying to think of something else to say. Nothing came.

"About sums it up, doesn't it?" she said to the empty room as she pushed the chair back and stood. She folded the letter and slid it into an envelope that she turned over in her hands several times before sealing.

"Alright then."

Back in the bathroom she started the water and squirted soap under the faucet before leaving the apartment to go downstairs. She carried the vodka with her, now a third empty, and stopped at the mailbox two blocks away, where she placed the envelope into the dark hole. She leaned forward and spoke to the gaping red mouth. "Shut up," she mumbled. "What do you care?"

Returning home, she locked the door but ignored the chain. Fog had covered the bathroom mirror, and bubbles had climbed halfway up the plastic-covered tub. She took an aspirin and sat on the toilet, watching the water. With every inch the suds rose, her heart rate increased. By the time the water reached the top, her breathing was labored. She rubbed her hands against her knees and soon reached for more vodka.

After turning off the water, Sharri stood and reached into a drawer for the box cutter she had taken from work. Leaning over the faucet, she ran hot water over the blade for several seconds and then delicately placed it on the side of the tub.

For several minutes she rested her hands on the sink and stared at the image in the foggy mirror. A dark, blurry ghost looked back. After another big drink, she began to remove her clothes, fold them, and place them on a shelf.

When everything was situated, she stepped into the warm water with one leg and then the other. Half way through the second step, someone knocked on the door. The sound startled Sharri, and she lost her balance. Reaching out, she caught the edge of the shelf and pulled it forward, breaking it away from the braces underneath. The shelf and her clothes fell to the floor along with her hair dryer, two bottles of lotion, and a handful of rollers.

Sharri froze.

Please go away. Just ... go away.

A few seconds later someone banged on the door again. A female voice spoke. "Sharri, are you here? It's Savannah."

What in the world?

Savannah was a new girl from work. She had been there three weeks, and their interaction had been limited to clocking in and clocking out—"How ya doing?"— "I'm good. You?"

What is she doing here?

"Just a minute!" Sharri wiped her face and threw on a robe. Closing off the bathroom, she took several deep breaths to calm herself. Latching the chain, she cracked the front door. Standing in the hall under yellow lights was a white girl with strawberry blonde hair and freckles. She was holding a two-liter bottle of grape soda and a bag of cookies.

"Hey girl! Surprise!" she said.

"Um, Savannah, what are you doing here?"

"Yeah, I know it's kind of weird, but I saw at work that you're always drinking this stuff and thought maybe you'd like some extra."

"Uh, yeah. Okay. Thanks. Well, listen ... I don't mean to be rude, but—"

"Oh, hey, don't worry. If this is a bad time I can come back later. It's fine," Savannah said and tried to look past Sharri into the apartment. "It sounded like a car wreck in there for a second. Is everything okay?"

Sharri moved closer to the crack in the door and closed the gap an inch or two. "Yeah, yeah. Sure. I just ... I just dropped some stuff when you knocked. It kind of startled me."

Savannah placed the two liter under her other arm and pushed her hair behind an ear. "Oh, okay, yeah, I do that kind of thing all the time." She noticed Sharri's left foot tapping on the linoleum floor and saw the nervous girl glance over her shoulder at the bathroom.

"So, you wanna just take this stuff and maybe we can get together some other time?"

Sharri thought about it for a second, and her grip tightened on the door. "Yeah, maybe we can do that. So ... uh, if you don't mind, just leave it there, and I'll get it later, okay?"

Savannah's eyebrows lowered. "Huh? Leave it here? In the hall?"

"Yeah, if you don't mind. Sorry, but I was just about to get in the bath."

"Yeah, okay. Sure thing."

"Thanks. And thanks for coming by."

"No problem. See ya later," Savannah said as she waved and turned to go.

Sharri locked the door and leaned against the frame. She placed one hand over her eyes and rubbed her temples. Several seconds passed.

There was another knock on the door.

Are you kidding me?

H.L. HUSSMANN

Sharri didn't move to unlock it and could hear the floor creak while Savannah shifted her weight from one foot to the other.

After an uncomfortable pause, Savannah's voice carried into the room.

"Sharri? Hey, it's okay if you don't want to open the door. But ... I mean ... I just wanted you to know something. Okay?"

Still no response.

"I hope this doesn't make me seem like a weirdo, but it's just that watching you at work sometimes it seems like maybe something is bothering you and you might be feeling lousy. So, I just wanted to tell you that I noticed. That's all."

Sharri stopped rubbing her head and pressed the back of her hand against her mouth.

"So anyway, I just wanted to let you know that even though I don't know you very well, I love you, and I've been praying for you. I don't know if that helps, but I thought I ought to tell you. Okay? I'll see you at work tomorrow."

After a minute of silence Savannah's footsteps moved away from the door and down the stairs.

Sharri tried to make sense of what had just happened. Her head was spinning from the vodka. It was hard to discern what was real.

She had thought of this night for years and had imagined bleeding out and slipping into oblivion in a warm bath thousands of times. This was supposed to be the night. How could Savannah knock on her door? Why would she do that?

And more, how could this be the first time in almost seventeen years that anyone had said those words to her?

"I love you."

Tears began flowing down Sharri's face as she reached for the chain on the door. Throwing it open, she stepped into the hall, pulled her robe above her ankles, and ran down the stairs and into the darkened street where Savannah was walking almost a block away.

The girl turned when she heard Sharri yelling.

"Savannah, wait!"

The next evening two police officers would arrive at Sharri's door to receive warm hugs from a crying girl and a story that surprised them both.

Eleven years later, Sharri and her husband would stand before parliament to share their vision for reform in the foster care system of South Africa. Five children would greet them when they returned home.

His business is healing people.

Aulus

H.L. HUSSMANN

LETTER SEVEN
Finding Him in Solitude

Beloved,

There is a well-known passage fulfilled in Heaven. It reads, "He makes me lie down in green pastures, he leads me beside still waters."

I have been blessed in the Kingdom of God with a place of solitude and stillness reserved only for me. It might be hard to imagine its size, but I can walk for years and never see its borders. It's a land of lush gardens with the softest grass. It contains beautiful foliage never seen on Earth. There are vast canyons and jagged-peaked mountains to explore. The air is crisper and cleaner than mountain air, and the birds and rivers join together making music. When I am there, it is only the God of all creation and me. I can sing where no one else can hear. I can dance where only He sees.

In that place is a luxurious field of grass that stretches out of sight in all directions. In the middle of that field is a lake of perfect stillness, with water so clear it can't be seen except for the reflection of Heaven's Light.

I have spent days on end there, alone with God. I sat with my feet in the water and thrilled at each breath. I dove to the bottom of the lake and viewed plants and fish no one else will ever see. I lay in the grass and stared at the clouds. But mostly, I listened.

The rule of that location is this: I am not allowed to speak. Not a word. There is a holiness and a stillness that forbid it. But it isn't difficult. In the presence of God, with that level of isolation, comes tranquility. I have never heard God speak more clearly than at that lake. But many times He, too, remains silent. He just is, and I just am, and that is good enough.

I remember how difficult it was to be alone in silence when I was on Earth. Whether it was work to be done, a crying child, or neighbors stopping by, something always seemed in the way. Even with many acres of farmland, finding solitude was a challenge.

It is worse for you today. In your world, words like *stillness*, *solitude*, *serenity*, and *meditation* have been replaced with *noise*, *activity*, *entertainment*, and *distraction*. Days of reading a book, taking a walk, and having lengthy conversations with God are rare. They have been substituted with frantic movement from appointment to appointment, free time filled with commotion, and a vulgar pursuit of diversion. Most Christians today rarely, if ever, sit in silence and wait on God. That valuable practice is nearly extinct.

The hunger for noise and distraction is cancer in the spirit of a man, and many are destroyed by a lack of stillness.

Imagine a couple in love. Consider their most intimate moments. Are they surrounded by people, or are they alone? Are they distracted or focused? Do they whisper in each other's ears, selecting their words with care, or do they blather on and on?

The Lord of the universe is a jealous Lover, and He desires your attention. But He will not force intimacy. You must surrender heart, soul, mind, and strength. Too many spread themselves open to the distractions of the world and let the enemy have his way. Very few find the deepest pleasure in the warm embrace of God. It is a place of passion, gentleness, and connection.

I pray your eyes will be open. Silence and solitude are needs in your life, and they cannot—they must not—be neglected.

When a man comes before a king, he would be a fool to make noise, to speak in haste, to interrupt, or to turn his attention to distractions nearby. A king deserves reverence, and reverence can be seen in silent attention.

Do you understand, my friend, that you live your life—every second—in the presence of the Great King? Do you have an acute awareness of His presence? He refuses to shout and will not conquer the surrounding din for you. You must decide. Decide to eliminate the noise of the temporary. Flee distraction. Give Him your attention. Solomon described this attentiveness:

Guard your steps when you go to the house of God. Go near to listen rather than to offer the sacrifice of fools, who do not know that they do wrong. Do not be quick with your mouth, do not be hasty in your heart to utter anything before God. God is in Heaven and you are on Earth, so let your words be few.

If you will be still, you will sense Him overtaking you. If you will be quiet, you will hear Him—hard to discern at first, but with increasing volume as you tune your ears. His presence is found in the streets of the largest city, and His voice can be heard through the roar of engines and the clamor of crowds, but awareness of such will always be practiced in rooms with closed doors and natural settings far from others. Isolation is the training ground for experiencing Him everywhere.

Heaven is not unaware of the enemy's schemes. Nothing takes God by surprise. One of the greatest attacks on the people of God involves little planning or coordination. It is chaos through noise. If a believer consistently chooses the commotion of the world over the presence of God, he is defeated. A man cannot embrace both a deafening world and a whispering lover.

On Earth, my wife had learned this well. Nearly every morning, before the children awoke, she would slide out of bed and make her way to the kitchen. On cool days she would rekindle the fire and sit in the stillness, staring at the flames, listening for the voice of God.

What would You have from me today?

Many times I would emerge from our bedroom to hear soft crying as she encountered His presence.

I never met a soul who seemed more in touch with the Spirit of Jesus Christ than she. I learned that when she gave advice, I did well to listen. I remember once, after meeting with God, she told me, "Aulus, I believe you should visit Marcius today." The man lived two hours away by horseback, but when I arrived, Marcius met me at the door and embraced me. "Pastor, I was praying you would come. My daughter is very sick. Please come inside."

Events like this were common in her life. She was the most compassionate person I knew, and the most in tune with the voice of God.

Dear friend, God desires to speak to you as He did to my wife. He wants you to know His mind and share in His thoughts. He desires intimacy. But it will never happen amidst distraction.

You must find a place of solitude—a place you go to escape the world. It might be a cemetery near your home, a park in your community, or a room with a door that locks, but you must go there often. It should be your favorite place.

The enemy will fight this. He will come against you hard and often, but you must not let him win. Choose to seek God.

You may need to start small—a minute here or there with no distraction—but work toward more. If you have too much going on to seek God, you have too much going on. You will find a moment with Him will satisfy you more than a thousand hours of diversion.

He is waiting.

Aulus

H.L. HUSSMANN

LETTER EIGHT
The Word is Life

Dear Friend,

I remember the first time I ever saw the written Word of God.

My wife, two children, and I had awakened before sunrise on a Saturday morning and traveled thirty-five miles on two horses, stopping only for food. We arrived about an hour past sundown. There were more than 200 believers gathered at a small and secluded barn. A crowd was seated on the dirt floor, and the people were pressed together with little room to move. We stood outside, trying to see over the dozens of others who arrived too late for a seat. Torches and lanterns shone through the doors and cracks in the walls, illuminating the surrounding woods in a dark orange glow. My son climbed on my shoulders for a better view. My wife Maria stood on the tips of her toes while holding our daughter.

We were sore from our journey, but the anticipation made our tired bodies a distant concern. The children had endured without complaint. Even at their age, they understood what was about to happen.

The man introducing himself was known by two names: the Latin *Silvanus* and the Greek, which you will recognize, *Silas*. I knew the danger of idolizing a man, but the temptation was strong.

He wore a brown tunic with a thin rope belt, and dust from the road still covered his clothes. He had been a Christian from the beginning and traveled with the Apostle Paul for many years, establishing churches throughout Europe and Asia. He had been beaten and imprisoned, and then set free by a miracle. He was working with the Apostle Peter as an assistant and had transcribed letters from both Peter and Paul.

It was difficult to believe I was looking at the man who, with mortal hands, had crafted the Word of God. And I knew what he carried with him—a copy of one of those letters. You will know it as the First Epistle of Peter.

After introductory remarks, he reached into his purse. "My dear brothers and sisters, I maintain little illusion as to the reason you have come," he said, "and it isn't my charm or my good looks." Many smiled and a few laughed, but none of us could take our eyes off the scroll he had removed. It seemed torture to wait while he unwrapped the leather binding. That moment will stay with me

H.L. HUSSMANN

forever. There was no sound except the flickering of torches. No one breathed.

Silas scanned the faces of the crowd as his fingers delicately unraveled the paper. People shifted to get a better view.

"Let us begin."

"Peter, an apostle of Jesus Christ, to God's elect ...."

As he read I felt overwhelmed. I hung on every word. He read of the glories of salvation, saying *"for a little while"* we would endure trials and suffering. The letter challenged us to be self-controlled—abstaining from sinful desires—and to be holy because God is holy. It said we should remember the sufferings of Christ and respond to persecution in like manner. It reminded us the end of all things was near and gave instructions for the family, the church, and the world. We were told to humble ourselves before God, as those who do so will be lifted up by Him. Peter signed off with, *"Greet one another with a kiss of love. Peace to all of you who are in Christ."* Silas stopped and waited. The crowd had been silent throughout the reading and then, as one, filled the area with noise. Some cheered. Some cried. Others embraced their families. Someone on the other side of the barn yelled, "Again! Read it again!" And others joined in. "Yes, please! Read it again!" One, a more brazen believer toward the front, raised his hands in the air and drew laughs from the people. "Come, man. Don't tease us, get to reading! And when you're done with that, read it again!"

Silas complied.

"Peter, an apostle of Jesus Christ, to God's elect ...."

Over the next two days my family and I slept on the ground outside the barn. I had the privilege of examining the document and spending time with Silas. My reading skills were poor, but he was patient. He guided me through the letter twice. We were surrounded by dozens who listened. I estimate he was present for eighty readings of the letter over those two days. I probably attended sixty of those. I was doing my best to commit it to memory, establishing at least the general content in my mind. It would be an honor to return to my village and convey the message to my church. The nights near the barn held little sleep. During the day I would listen to the letter being read and talk with fellow ministers. At night I perfected the outline in my mind and reviewed it again and again.

The night before we returned home, I stayed up carving a block of wood from a nearby tree. With fire, a chisel, and the help of a friend, I etched my favorite portion into the hard wood.

Therefore, since Christ suffered in his body, arm yourselves also with the same attitude, because whoever suffers in the body is done with sin. As a result, they do not live the rest of their earthly lives for evil human desires, but rather for the will of God.

H.L. HUSSMANN

I had already memorized this, but the block of wood became my prized possession. I kept it wrapped in cloth and hidden away while traveling. When we came home, I dug a special place near my garden, bordered it with stone, and wrapped the block in resin-coated sheepskin. I placed it inside and covered the hole with grass and leaves. Every week I would take another chisel and a new fire and freshen the letters. For the next two years I would begin my day by removing the block of wood from its hiding place. Every morning I was challenged by the words. What does it mean to have the attitude of Christ? How do I live like that? How does suffering in the body do away with sin? How can I live only for the will of God? This short passage came alive to me in new ways, and each time I greeted it with anticipation. I knew I would hear from God.

In those days we revered the Word. There were some who dedicated their lives to studying the copies of those letters. They would memorize them line by line and travel to the churches, teaching the believers. It was too dangerous to carry copies, but soldiers could not arrest them for what they stored in their minds.

This might be hard to believe, but before I died I had memorized every word of the letter Silas presented that night. I also had committed to memory the book you know as Paul's letter to the Romans and portions of two letters Paul had written to Corinth. My family and congregation had memorized much as well.

In the early Church we were passionate about the written Word of God. We would risk death to read just a portion. Today, to an extent, I feel how God's heart aches at the lack of passion in the Church. The way most Christians treat their Bibles is hard to watch.

As I observe believers around the world I see Bibles that haven't been used in weeks or months. I see the Word of God thrown under the seats or into the trunks of cars and covered with tools or sporting goods. I have even seen people prop their feet up on the Word. If you ask believers today, "Where is your Bible?" many could not tell you. I see those who claim the name of Jesus read magazines, watch television, and scour the internet, and yet many of the same make little time for the living and enduring Word of God.

In Heaven are many of us who would have risked anything—and I do mean anything, no sacrifice would have been too great—for the opportunity Christians have today. There are not just a few verses at your disposal, not just a handful of letters. You have the completed Word of God. Many have multiple copies in different translations, and because it is readily available, it is treated as a common book. But it is special. It is precious. It is beyond valuable.

H.L. HUSSMANN

I hear Christians say, "I don't read the Bible like I should."

Access to the Bible is a gift, not a duty. Use of the word "should" is foolishness.

I pray the Word will never be your burden or obligation, but instead, your hobby and delight.

Before I end this letter I want to tell you one other story of a man who came to view it as such.

After the fall of Vietnam in 1973, a Vietnamese Christian named Hien Pham was captured near his home and transferred to a work camp. He was accused of lending aid to the Americans and was imprisoned without a trial.

For fourteen hours of the day, when he wasn't working the fields, he stayed in a concrete cell too narrow for him to lie down. The heat and humidity during the day and the incessant mosquitoes at night threatened his sanity. But worse was the propaganda. At all times, whether knee deep in a rice paddy or sitting alone in his cell, he was hearing communistic and atheistic teachings. In every hallway and on poles in the fields, loudspeakers blared the teachings of Karl Marx and Friedrich Engels. With no other voices in his head, after months of the broadcasts, the teachings took their toll. He questioned God, and after a year and a half of labor, tedium, and indoctrination, he caved in. One night in his cell he renounced the Father. He determined not to think about God from that day forward and left his faith behind.

The next morning he was assigned the worst job in the camp—emptying the prison latrines. There were no flush toilets, so emptying the waste and removing it from camp was a demoralizing task rotated among the prisoners. Each man was given a small portion of water daily, but in the oppressive heat, water was a precious commodity, and little could be used for hygiene. When assigned this task, a man knew the odors and filth would cling to him for days.

The latrines were holes cut into wooden boxes. Prisoners were expected to remove the waste with buckets and haul it to the edge of camp. Avoiding the sewage was impossible.

After three hours of work, Hien Pham noticed something odd in one of the boxes. It was a single piece of paper, smeared with human waste. It was too dirty to read, but he could see enough characters to tell it was written in English. He had studied English at Saigon University in the early '60s but had not seen English characters since his arrival at the camp. Looking around with caution, he reached into the box, grabbed the paper, and shoved it into his pants.

That night he sat cross-legged on the floor of his cell with his back to the metal door. He wiped down the paper and began to read. His hands began shaking.

We know that in all things God works for the good of those who love Him, who have been called according to

H.L. HUSSMANN

His purpose ... for I am convinced that neither death nor life, neither angels nor demons, neither the present nor the future, nor any powers, neither height nor depth, nor anything else in all creation, will be able to separate us from the love of God that is in Christ Jesus our Lord.

Hien fell to his knees and repented of his despair. He spent the night in prayer. Sunrise found him pacing his cell, anxious for more work.

That morning, he approached the cell block commander and requested to be taken out of the fields and placed on permanent latrine duty. He couldn't stop smiling. The commander assumed the prisoner was losing his mind and, in amusement at the request, consented. Day after day, week after week, Hien emptied the latrines, often whistling or singing while he worked—reinforcing the commander's opinion. The combination of his apparent insanity and the constant smell of human waste caused the guards to avoid him. It became easy, on a daily basis, to sift through the boxes and search for more paper. It was nauseating, but every few days he would find a new page. One of the prison guards was using a Bible for toilet paper. What he found, he hid in his cell, where none of the soldiers wanted to enter. His nights were spent reading the Bible and seeking the face of God, Who soon arranged a miraculous escape that included other prisoners.

This man endured ridicule, defilement, and backbreaking labor to read God's Word. When he escaped less than 200 days later, he took sixty pages of the New Testament with him. When he died, those same soiled pages were by his side in the casket. He had memorized them all.

I spoke with Hien Pham while preparing this letter, and he took me to his home. There he related the details of his story and showed me the pages on display. They are a rare material gift that has been brought here. The stains remain, but like everything else, they have been made pure.

So many today cannot get past laziness, self-absorption, and love of pleasure to adore God's Word. I pray it will not be so in your life.

May it be your lifeline.

Aulus

LETTER NINE
Sending and Receiving

Dearest One,

We pray here.

Prayer is communication with God, and in Heaven it is constant and takes many forms.

There is a temple where we seek God on a personal level but also participate in the process of prayer between Earth and Heaven.

The temple is the size of your greatest cities. Some rooms are large enough for millions to gather. The acoustics are perfect, and when we pray the reverberations are like hands, kneading and massaging us as we enter God's presence and participate in His cause.

Other rooms are small and create an atmosphere of peaceful confinement, but they contain doors to worlds of solitude as I previously described. It is the prayer hub of Heaven, and its spokes extend through the Universe.

When I am there I can "tune in" to the prayers reaching Heaven. Like radio waves in the air, I can focus and, in a flash, catch them. I have done so for weeks at a time.

A mother prays for her little girl.

A worker complains about his boss.

A young boy asks what is ridiculous.

When I hear what is incoming, I am able to see Heaven's response, and by this learn more of God. The waves of prayer are processed and sent back. It is how they are returned that helps me understand Him. I learn how they are answered, and I begin to play a part. When I think like God, and participate with Him to answer, it is as if we are sorting and sending. The Lord is sovereign, but He delegates His authority as I am submitted to Him.

Let me tell you about the examples above:

The mother prays for her little girl, that one day she would be a great woman and tell many about Jesus. It's a simple prayer and seems insignificant. But her heart is knit with God's, and her passion is God's Kingdom. The answer is "yes." I sense God's pleasure. I know His purpose. God plants seeds of blessing that, years later, will come to pass. Only He knows the specifics, but instead of failure, the girl will see success. She will have strength in hardship. She will meet the right people at the right time. She will have advantages others do not.

The worker complains about his boss. His complaint is legitimate. His boss is not a fair man. But the worker has missed God's heart and cannot see God's purpose. He is unthankful and unmerciful toward his superior, who has trials of his own. God wants to change the situation, but His greater purpose is twofold: filling the worker with thanksgiving, and giving the boss every chance at healing. The answer is "no," but the response is not of the ignoring kind. God sends His touch toward the worker's heart—a gift of love for his boss, appreciation for his job, and contentment beyond circumstance. But it is the worker's responsibility to receive. If he wants only immediate change in his situation, he will be disappointed, but if he is laying the situation at God's feet, he will receive an answer that is better than "yes." When the answer is "no," it is always accompanied by something better. Always.

And the little boy?

God sent him a package of gifts just for staying in touch. And He does the same for you when you are ridiculous.

Every prayer brings treasure. Every time you focus on Him, directing your thoughts, making requests, or just saying "thanks," He sends a response. And it isn't just acknowledgment. He doesn't only say, "yes," "no," or "later." He always sends something real and practical.

A man is praying now.

He is pacing in his room. He tries to speak, but his mind interferes.

"God ... I ...." *What's the use? God knows that already.*

He continues pacing. But the communication is a start, and God responds.

"Tell me anyway. Trust me." He sends the man power to let go of his need to impress.

But the man does not receive. He stares at the ceiling, determined to find the right words.

"Why is this so difficult, God?"

And God sends another box of grace. *"Stop trying to do it right. It's impossible. Look at me."*

This time the man opens the corner of the box—enough to peer inside. He falls to his knees and places his hands on the floor.

"I can't even pray, God. Help me."

"Now we are getting somewhere. What can I do?"

You may see prayer as one-sided. You pray, and God listens. But that view is not clear. Prayer is lopsided, but not in the direction you think. There is more interaction on His part than yours. But His large part cannot come into play without your small one. You come to Him offering little, and He moves into action. Prayer brings change. Prayer always causes God to do what He would not do otherwise.

Let me say it again. Communication with God always causes Him to do something He would not do otherwise. He will not change His purposes when we pray, but He will, with certainty, change

His actions. He has created mankind to participate in His Kingdom, and one way is through prayer.

One writer on Earth said it like this:

God cannot do something unless we work. He stores the hills with marble, but He has never built a cathedral. He fills the mountains with iron ore, but He never makes a needle or a jet airplane. He leaves that to us. If then, God has left many things dependent on man's thinking and working, why should He not leave some things dependent upon man's praying? He has done so .... We cannot suppose that God will do for us without prayer what He has promised to do for us only through prayer.

Talk with God, and you can impact foreign lands more than if you walked the streets. Missionaries will fear nothing. Young men will flee temptation. Money will pour into the hands of the faithful. And dark powers that bombard the nations of Earth like flak will be rendered impotent. Sunlight will part the battlefields and fill the lives of men and women everywhere.

As I watch the Church today, I see few who study prayer, fewer still who practice, and even fewer who master the art of sharing God's ear and moving His hand. It is talked about often and toyed at a little, but it is rarely pursued. And two words describe the reason: time and doubt.

Christians in the present day do not make time to pray. Why? Because they don't believe it works, and they value time above all. In secret recesses, many question whether God hears. And if He hears, they doubt He will move. They have failed to receive God's response so many times that they have given up asking. They have begun on the path that brings change but never followed through with the sending and receiving process. And now, they pray only when they must to maintain the appearance of piety or to appease their guilt. But prayers born of self-righteousness and guilt are returned to the sender with a note: *"Be free!"* And the note is rarely received.

But how can you pray?

How can you conquer the doubt?

It is through Him. Like every other victory you will achieve, it will be His power, accepted, that breaks the chains.

My suggestion is this: say anything to God. No matter how trivial, angry, childish, or selfish—just say it. Then wait and listen. He will always answer.

You might say, "I never hear You."

He will respond, *"But you are hearing Me now."*

You might cry in pain for your losses.

He will say, *"Come to Me. Rest."*

You might say, "Leave me alone!"

And He will say, *"I will be here for a while, waiting for you to change your mind. But don't delay."*

Whatever He says, receive it. Learn from it. Do what He says. Respond to what He tells you and then wait again. If you question what you are hearing, turn to His Word for confirmation. Turn to others who know Him well.

Soon, you will see that the hindrance to your prayers has never come from God's side. As you open the door of communication with Him, He will give you power to open it further. As you admit your dependence on Him, He will prove you right. You are needy, but He will fill your need. Your only part in the process is availability. That is something He will not force.

The rest is on Him, and He will not fail.

Aulus

H.L. HUSSMANN

LETTER TEN
The Parable of the Well

Beloved,

Today I offer a parable.

An ancient Assyrian king designed a test to separate the worthy from the unworthy in his armies, and the highest military positions were offered to those who passed. Many tried and failed. Some did not survive.

Contestants were given no information. They were stripped and blindfolded before entering a dark hall. Thick sand soon greeted their bare feet. Within moments, light shone through the blindfold as the heat of a scorching sun swarmed over dark skin. A gate nearby slammed shut.

"Uncover your eyes."

It would take many seconds for a man's vision to adjust while he squinted under cupped hands.

The circular pit was a hundred feet across, and the contestant's vantage point made it unclear if it had been built on top of the ground or dug into the earth. A wall of block and mortar bordered the field of sand with only one exit, which was covered with dark bronze bars. The wall was twenty feet high with a guard at each compass point. Between two of the guards sat the king, shaded and fanned by servants.

In the center of the area was a water well. Constructed of the same material as the wall, it jutted three feet out of the ground and formed a circle nine feet in diameter.

"The rules are simple," announced a herald standing near the king. "Your feet may not leave the sand, and your hands may not touch it. Now, drink from the well and live."

As new contestants surveyed the area, each step came with difficulty in the thick, hot sand. To keep from burning, each would shift his legs from side to side and dig in several inches.

In most cases, the challenger would approach the well, place his hands on the blocks, and stare into the dark hole. The cool, clear water was seven feet away—an impossible distance even for the tallest. Some would lean so that only their toes touched the sand, but none could reach his goal.

Others would stand and stare without reaching. It was clear the distance was too great.

In every challenge the contestant eventually would retreat from the well to the small amount of shade the walls provided. As the day progressed, the shade shrank to nothing and then

H.L. HUSSMANN

began again on the opposite wall. For much of the day it was not enough to cover the entire body. Skin would blister as the tongue swelled from thirst. At times, the test would run through the first night, and the king would remain, stoic and patient, for the contest to end the next day.

Many who tried would sit in silence and stare at the well. Some would grind their teeth and glare at the king. Others would cry. And some would, eventually, beg for their lives.

"My lord, please, have mercy."

When this happened, the king would nod to his herald, who would stand and announce, "Your king will spare you; however, you may never return to your life before. If you accept, you will remain in the palace as a servant."

The offer was almost always taken, though some would suffer for hours before yielding.

For those who never sought mercy there was only one alternative. Some hurled insults and cursed the king. But all of those, in time, hurled themselves into the well and drowned.

But not all failed. After many contests, with most men accepting servitude and a handful meeting death, one man succeeded.

When this man entered the arena he behaved like the others. He examined the well, searched the walls, dug himself into the coolest sand, and sat with his back to the wall and his arms around his knees. Instead of baking in the sun for hours, though, he soon stood and addressed the king.

Walking halfway to the well, he dug his feet in and bowed his head, staring at the sand below.

"Great king. May I speak?"

The king leaned forward and examined the contestant. Soon, he nodded to the herald.

"Proceed."

"My lord," the man began, "I have known some who have served close to you, and they are good men who describe you as wise and kind."

He looked up and swept one arm around at the walls. "I cannot complete this task. It clearly is designed to illustrate my inability. However, I have seen the way you govern, and I believe you desire I succeed."

At this, the man dropped to one knee. "My king, please help me. What should I do?" And he waited with head bowed.

The king motioned to his herald, who walked away and soon returned with a wooden bucket.

"Rise," the king said.

When the man was back on his feet the king took the bucket and threw it into the arena.

"Good soldier. Now drink."

He grabbed the bucket and hurried to the water's edge to reach as far as he could, his hips balanced on the rock wall and his toes stretched into the sand. But he could only brush the surface of the water. He brought the bucket up to his mouth and placed the bottom against his lips, the damp wood offering some relief. Shaking it above his face, three drops of water fell on his tongue.

The bronze gate rumbled. The man looked to see the herald standing on the edge of the wall.

"Congratulations," the herald said and motioned toward the exit. He began clapping, and the soldiers followed suit. One soldier said, "Well done!" Another yelled, "Yes! Yes!"

Setting the bucket on the blocks, the man stood and walked toward the dark hall, anxious to move into the cool shade.

Two steps from the exit he paused to look at the king, who wasn't clapping but maintained a polite smile.

"My lord, is there something more?"

The king said nothing but glanced at the well and back at the man. A soldier had appeared from behind the open gate and extended his hand. "You may exit, friend."

But the contestant waited, looking at the king and then at the well.

"Wait."

Turning, he went back to the short block wall and peered inside. The water was so inviting that even with the exit available, he wanted nothing more than to jump in. Out of the corner of his eye he saw the king shift forward in his seat.

In a moment of revelation the man moved. He took the bucket and plunged it into the sand, scooping up as much as he could without touching it. He dumped the sand into the well, and ripples bounced out to the wall and back.

Before they could subside, another bucketful landed. It was followed by another.

The soldiers became still as he worked. The sun beat down. Sweat fell from the man's forehead and nose as he threw bucket after bucket into the well. The water began to rise.

For more than an hour he shoveled, stopping at times to dip the bottom of the vessel and wet his lips and face. Soon the water rose to a good level. He plunged his bucket under the liquid and filled it to the top. And standing, he shouted as he raised it above his head and poured cool water over his face and body.

Some who entered the arena perished. Others survived as servants in the house of the king.

A few wet their tongues and became leaders and managers in the kingdom.

But rarely, a man would not only complete the challenge, he would be one of the few who conquered it. He would become one of the most powerful men in all the king's lands—a ruler over tribes and nations and a constant companion of his master.

Those who have ears, let them hear.

Aulus

H.L. HUSSMANN

LETTER ELEVEN
Saved From the Cold

Dear Child,

Now named Krakow, Poland, the city of Wawel Hill was fast becoming a center of political and economic activity in the middle of the known world. There, in AD 1013, a young man was killed for his faith.

Eight-year-old Mieszko Nowak had lost both his parents when invaders raided their village. He retreated to Wawel Hill and for five years lived on the streets. He ate from garbage carts and stole food when possible. In the bitter cold winters he would retreat to the lowest parts of the city, where he and dozens of other children would burn trash and huddle around fires.

On one of the coldest nights of his life, he was crammed together with eight others sharing four blankets. Their breath could be seen in the firelight, and the youngest would not stop crying, which set the whole group on edge.

"Shut her up, will ya!" Mieszko said to the girl's brother, who clutched her against his chest. "Do it! Or I'll do it myself."

He was skin and bones but older and taller than the other boy, who whispered in the girl's ear. She snuggled closer and whimpered.

For the next two hours, sleep would come and go. When one child moved, others awoke.

Mieszko's best friend, Fillip, shook him from his half-sleep. "Miesz, look. Someone's here."

Mieszko's vision was blurred, and he heard the crunch of footsteps in the snow before he saw their owner. Stepping out of the darkness was an old man. His dark wool overtunic covered layers of clothing and a large frame. A fur cap covered his ears, and tattered mittens peeked from his sleeves. He stopped twenty feet away and surveyed the group, only half of whom looked back. He hesitated as if making an important decision, took a deep breath, and pressed forward.

Mieszko sat up on his elbows and pushed farther into the warm bodies around him as the man approached. When the glow of the fire bounced off the man's weathered face, the boy saw track lines from tears that had vanished in thick facial hair.

Close enough to touch, the man squatted before the group. He placed his elbows on his legs and uncovered his hands. Another tear slid

H.L. HUSSMANN

down his cheek as he looked from face to face. One of the smaller children elbowed Mieszko under the blanket.

"What do you want, old man?" Mieszko said with a bravado he didn't feel.

The man fixed his eyes on the boy and moved to a position on his knees, much closer than before. With children on each side, Mieszko had nowhere to go as the man reached for him with both hands. He tried to turn away, but the man placed a hand on each side of the boy's face and gazed at him under bushy eyebrows speckled white. The man's dark brown eyes reminded the boy of his father.

Still holding him, the man glanced again at each of the other children. Mieszko could feel the warm, calloused hands trembling.

"Boy, will you come with me?"

He would never understand why he consented, but on such a night as that, anywhere was an improvement. The old man took his hand, pulled him from the freezing group, and led him away. Before he departed he turned to those remaining.

"I'm sorry, children. May God make a way."

Mieszko would always remember how the man sobbed as they left the others behind.

The man was poor but not starving. He lived with his wife in a shanty village, where they prepared food in a community cookhouse. They had very little, but from that day forward they shared what they had with the boy, who slept on a bed of leaves the woman had sewn into a bag.

The old man often would joke, "We've got thousands of things to eat, my child, but sadly, they're all beans." He would laugh and slap his leg while the old woman rolled her eyes.

His warmth and humor soon won the boy over, and Mieszko began to call him "dedko," or "grandpa."

Their nights were spent around a fire in the floor of their home. Mieszko's responsibility was to keep the embers burning—a job that required scrounging the city and local woods for materials. But it was better than scrounging for food.

It was during those nights, while smoke snaked through a hole in the roof, that Dedko would tell him stories of the Christ.

"Sit with me, boy," he would say. Mieszko would lean on the old man's shoulder as the narratives began. Many nights he would fall asleep and dream of lepers healed and little boys raised from the dead. And in the days that followed he talked to God.

On one of those evenings, as the boy listened to the story of the prodigal son for the third time, he leaned farther into the old man and tilted his head to look at him. Dedko was prodding the flames with a stick and staring through the fire as if watching the characters in the story.

"Dedko?"

The old man paused. "What is it, child?"

"Why me?" It was a question he had longed to ask but never had worked up the courage.

"What do you mean?"

"Why did you choose me, Dedko? Why not the other children? Not that I am complaining, but why leave the others behind? Or, why not take one of the younger ones who couldn't fend for himself?"

Dedko's brow furrowed, and he scratched at the ground with the stick, taking several seconds. Just when the boy thought no answer was coming, the old man placed his hand on Mieszko's head and stroked his hair.

"You were the first to speak. It had to be you."

"I still don't understand," Mieszko said. "What do you mean?"

"I watched you all for quite a while that night," Dedko said, and forced a slight smile. "You were all so cold and so ... helpless ...." The old man's eyes misted, and his voice wavered as he turned his face from the boy. "I had told the Lord I would take one of you home. As you know, we have little, but what we have we give to God. We knew we could help one, but more seemed impossible. So I prayed as I watched. Finally, I told Him whichever one of you spoke to me first would be the one." He pulled the boy closer and kissed him on the head.

Over the next few years, the boy would grow into a fine young man. He was a friend to Jesus and to many people. It was common for him to fast two days a week to take his share to other orphans in the streets. His friend Fillip soon became a Christian as well. Fillip continued to live without a home but would often sleep by Dedko's fire. The man referred to him as his "adopted son's adopted son." And as the boys grew into their teens together, they developed a passion for sharing the message of Jesus. Neither knew it would lead to one of their deaths, but it wouldn't have stopped them.

But that is a story for my next letter.

For now, I hope you will learn from the old man. He and his wife had almost nothing. It would have been easy to justify keeping what they had for themselves. Few would blame them. And yet they paid the price to rescue one boy, who, as you will see, rescued many.

You cannot help everyone.

But you can rescue some.

Many Christians today want more—more land, more rooms, more money. But they fail to offer what they already have to God—which always will involve offering it to others. So few adopt, and very few take in the homeless, orphans, and widows. Many call it "wisdom" and say "it's not my ministry." But I am in a position to see the intentions of the heart. "Wisdom" is often an excuse to cover apathy and a lack of love.

Yes, use wisdom, and yes, take care of what God has entrusted to you—namely, your family. But never let these aspects of true Godliness be used as an excuse to avoid sacrifice. Jesus was the wisest of the wise and the Creator of the family. Yet He gave all.

I realize one cannot change a country or a culture overnight, and the culture of Christianity today is far removed from the early days of sharing everything. But I also know what is right and that one person can bring change. One family's sacrifice can make a difference, and I don't mean token offerings that are given from abundance. I am speaking of the "take-up-your-cross-and-follow-me" kind of offerings. The specifics will be different for every believer, but the dynamic of death to self is the same.

What has God asked of you, child?

Whatever it is, the correct answer is always, "Yes, Lord. Whatever You say." Even when it means missing vacations, driving less of a car, or missing out on the latest cultural obsession.

One day you will see that what you thought was sacrifice was no sacrifice at all.

If you could see the view from my desk, you would understand. But more on that later.

It all will perish.

Aulus

H.L. HUSSMANN

LETTER TWELVE
Compel Them to Come In

Friend,

In the southern district of Mieszko's city was an area that locals called the "Grease."

In the Grease, the lower ends of society could shop for wares and dine from the carts of men serving unrecognizable cuts of meat to those who could afford no other kind.

"Pure meat, my friends! Pure meat! And for you ... half off!"

The spattering from their carts and the smoke of their fires filled the area at all hours, day and night, causing the Grease to reek of burned fat and oils.

In the Grease, people could have their pocketbooks "greased" through blatant thievery or the work of con artists. Most in the area were "greased" every night as they drowned their sorrows in mead and ale. And "greased" was a vulgar term describing the goings on between a prostitute and her john.

Mieszko and Fillip were becoming fixtures in the Grease. It was three weeks past Mieszko's seventeenth birthday, and for several months the boys had been coming to the area to share the love of Jesus. Moving through the crowds, they would approach people standing or sitting alone and offer prayer or conversation. At times their efforts were productive, but often the people were too drunk to comprehend, so the boys would pray and move on. At other times they were mocked and jeered at for their efforts. The regulars in the area called them "priests."

"Hey, priest! Pray for me! Pray she'll give me a discount!"

There were those who admired the two, and on some occasions people approached and asked for prayer—a sick child, a contracted disease, and, once or twice, a way out of the Grease.

But Mieszko had grown discouraged by the lack of tangible response. He wanted more. And on that night, in the cool of autumn, he tried something new.

"If I throw up, at least it's common here," he told Fillip as the boys watched the crowd from a dark alcove. Mieszko ran his hands over his legs as he prayed out loud. "God, give me strength. I am Yours. Whatever You want. I'll do it."

In the hour they had been praying they had seen one fight that ended with a shattered nose and blood staining the dirt below. They had seen a man run into an alley, chasing three boys who had stolen from him, and they had watched dozens of men enter the "greasehouse" nearby.

Fillip stood and paced in the shadows.

"If you're going to do this, Miesz, maybe we should come back earlier in the day when things are calmer. We could come back tomorrow afternoon. There will be less of a crowd and–" Glancing at his friend, Fillip knew his comments had set something off in the older boy, who was shaking his head and clenching his jaw while staring at the people.

"No, Fillip. It's now. I have to do this. And you're right. In the afternoon no one's here."

Before Fillip could protest, Mieszko rose from the crate he had brought with him and walked into the open air beyond the alcove. Despite legs that threatened to give way, he placed the box on the ground and stepped up on it. He was a head and a half above the tallest man there, and his chest was moving in and out rapidly as he wrung his hands and surveyed the crowd. Very few had noticed him.

Whispering a quiet prayer, the boy summoned his courage, leaned his head back, and shouted as loud as he could.

"I DON'T WANT TO TALK TO YOU TODAY!"

The crowd quieted and turned their heads in his direction. Three drunken men who had been singing paused.

"And do you know why?" Mieszko continued. His voice carried across the courtyard and bounced off the block walls. "It's because I'm afraid! I'm afraid to stand here. I'm afraid of giving offense, or that you will think me a fool."

A man stumbling by yelled back. "You ARE a fool!" Several in the crowd laughed, and another yelled at the drunk man, "You would know, Bolek!" which drew more laughter.

Mieszko continued, "But I have decided that with God's help I will not live my life based on fear. It is too easy to let others dictate what I do or don't do. I've found that my fears are rooted in selfishness, and that is no way to go through life. I am afraid of your opinions because I love ME, not you! And I don't want to live my life based on fear OR selfishness. Do you?"

While he preached, a nearby vendor had ceased shouting at the crowd. Several men had stopped walking and stood to listen. A prostitute had emerged from her building and was standing on the steps, arms crossed. Another was leaning out her window.

This is working.

"You may have heard of another, much greater than I, who refused a selfish life," Mieszko said. "His name was Jesus, and He lived a thousand years ago. He was a great teacher and much more.

When someone asked this wisest of men what was most important in life, He responded. First, He said to love God with all your heart, soul, mind, and strength." At this, Mieszko pointed both hands to the sky and noticed several in the crowd follow his view. "And second, love others like you love yourself." He pointed around at the faces in the crowd. "Love people!"

Two more girls joined the first on the steps of the greasehouse. Some in the crowd walked away, but others remained. Beyond the immediate crowd, the hustle of the Grease was resuming.

"This Jesus said life was meant to be lived outside of me. Loving God is outside of me. And loving you is as well. Any who are honest know this is right. No one wants to arrive at his death and think back to how selfish he was. THERE IS MORE TO LIFE THAN LIVING FOR MYSELF! Everything I've ever done that I'm ashamed of has been a result of my selfishness."

A man emerged from the greasehouse, straightening his clothes, and grabbed one of the girls by the shoulder. Whispering in her ear, he pulled her toward the door and swatted her in the leg with his cane. She ran into the entry room and was soon followed by the other two, both of whom stayed close to an open window nearby. The cane tapped each step as the man descended.

"Jesus claimed that none of us can escape selfishness without help. And He claimed to be that help. He claimed to be the Messiah of God,

God-in-the-flesh, who came to save us. He taught that when we open our lives and hearts to Him, He will do a miracle and give us a new beginning. He said you can be 'born again' and start over. You can escape how your life is now."

The man pushed his way through the crowd and stood within steps of Mieszko's crate, folding his cane under his arm. Two large men made their way to stand behind him as he yelled.

"And what is wrong with the life I'm living now, eh?" the man exclaimed.

Mieszko paused.

Well-known in the Grease, Rostek Czerwinski was the "owner" of most of the girls in the greasehouses, and many of the vendors and store owners paid him a percentage of their profits. The boys had avoided him thus far, hearing stories of what he had done to those who had crossed him. He was short and balding but broad across the shoulders and, by all accounts, mean as a boar.

Mieszko looked at Rostek for a moment and weighed his options. He had been concerned about the man's arrival and had prayed about how to handle the possible confrontation.

"Speak up, boy!"

Several in the crowd were fidgeting. A few began moving away.

"Mister Czerwinski, I'm glad you are here," Mieszko said, still projecting his voice. "I am aware of the admiration people have for you in the Grease. And I was hoping I could–"

Rostek leaned his head back and laughed out loud, cutting Mieszko off. The man elbowed one of his companions and said, loud enough for the crowd to hear, "Get him, will ya! They ADMIRE me here."

His friends laughed, and a few in the crowd forced smiles. But then Rostek's eyes narrowed, and he took a step toward the boy.

"I will say this once," he said, pulling his cane from under his arm and tapping it against the crate. "You are costing me money, boy." He glanced at the windows above. "Look!"

Several of the girls inside had their windows open, and when the bald man looked up, they vanished back into their rooms. One drunken john remained, arms resting on the windowsill. His bloodshot eyes were trying to focus on the scene below. Rostek nodded his head toward the door and said, "Get them back to work. I can handle this one." One of the men turned and advanced toward the building.

Mieszko's heart was pounding, and his mouth was dry. He noticed Fillip had moved closer to his side. He straightened his shoulders and looked at the man, praying for words. Somehow, instead of seeing the cruel monster so many had described, he was filled with compassion. Standing before him was a fat, frightened child who had never known love.

Looking back at the windows, Miesko shouted. "Yes, sir. I do see the pause given to those you abuse. And I thank God for one moment of peace for them while their miserable lives are interrupted. I praise the God of Heaven for such a gift."

Rostek was turning red-faced and gripping his cane with white knuckles.

"And you, sir, have the influence to bring more such peace into their lives–"

"Shut up!"

"–if you would only–"

"Shut up, boy!"

"–look at yourself and see–"

"Do you know what I am going to do to you?"

But Mieszko continued. "I do not fear you. What can you take from me? But know this: While you have hurt many, I see that you, too, have been hurt. May you somehow see that the God and Father of the Lord Jesus Christ loves you, the abuser, as much as he does the abused."

Looking up to the open windows, Mieszko shouted. "There is freedom for the abused! Seek God and find Him." Then, pointing his finger at Rostek, "And you, too, repent and turn to Him, for He loves you dearly."

A maniacal cry erupted from Rostek's chest as he closed the distance between himself and the boy, clenching the cane in his fists. His face was filled with blood, and the skin on his brow pulled against bulging veins. Fillip tried to step in, but the man moved too fast.

Lowering his shoulders and pushing forward, Rostek strained and grunted as he launched himself upward. He caught Mieszko just above the hips with both fists, pushing his arms and the cane forward, knocking Mieszko from his perch.

Later, Fillip could remember every detail of the next few seconds. He could see the screaming man and could visualize the attack. But the image that remained burned in his mind was of his friend's head bleeding and his eyes growing dim. Mieszko had flown into the air behind the crate and skidded several feet before his head whipped back and cracked against the corner of the dark alcove's rock steps.

Moments later Mieszko's head was in Fillip's lap as the younger boy clung to his friend.

"Miesz!"

"Miesz, wake up! Stay with me!"

Rostek moved behind Fillip and grabbed him by his collar. Spit flew from purple lips as he pulled the boy's head backward.

"It's a shame your friend *fell* like that, isn't it?" He shook the boy. "I'm talking to you! He fell, didn't he?"

Fillip was in shock.

"Yes, sir. He fell. Yes."

With one more jerk, Rostek pushed him toward the ground. "And don't forget it. Do you understand?"

Fillip was nodding between sobs as Rostek turned to the crowd, most of whom had vanished into alleys and buildings nearby. He pulled a cloth from his pocket and wiped his forehead while placing the cane back under his arm.

"Such a travesty," he said as he walked back toward his building. "Such a young, innocent boy—and so clumsy."

He made eye contact with several in the crowd.

"A travesty, right?"

"Yes, sir."

"A clumsy boy, correct?"

"Very clumsy, sir."

Three days later Mieszko's body would be burned. The activities in the Grease would continue for years.

So, here is my question to you, beloved:

Did the boy fail?

Was he obeying God or acting on impulse? Were his efforts helpful, or did they do more harm than good? Should he have acted differently?

The answer will be clear in my next letter.

Praise God for those who gave all.

Aulus

LETTER THIRTEEN
Redemption

Beloved,

Rostek Czerwinski eventually spent nine years in prison for the death of Mieszko Nowak.

It took Mieszko's adopted father Dmitri more than two years to find justice. Fillip and the old man continued spending time on the outskirts of the Grease. They talked about Jesus with those who would listen, and they questioned girls from the greasehouse when they could find them alone. They sometimes had been threatened and bullied for their efforts. But after months of searching and pressing the local constable, Dmitri and Fillip had Czerwinski brought before a judge.

The judge showed little mercy when, in addition to Fillip, three others testified to what they had seen. Two of the witnesses were prostitutes. One had come to follow Jesus, and both saw Rostek's prosecution as the only way to escape the Grease. The other eyewitness was a vendor from the crowd. All three spoke to the judge in private. Compelled by the old man, even Fillip did so. Only Dedko had stood at the public trial, summarizing the testimonies of the others.

Nine years should have been a death sentence in the labor camps. Forced to dig for coal hundreds of miles from Wawel Hill, prisoners were shackled together at all times. Food was an afterthought, and disease waited in the shadows of the mines, overtaking the condemned one by one. Dysentery, beri beri, and tuberculosis crept from one prisoner to the next. Rostek had been shackled to more than twenty men through the years, and many had perished in pools of their own waste and blood. He survived through violence, killing when he had to and threatening often. Through intimidation, bribes, and a connection with the outside world, he ate twice the normal rations and rested when he was sick. Thoughts of revenge consumed his mind and drove him to survive.

He arrived back home in no shape to retake the Grease, but he connected with old associates. He had lost most of his weight, and skin hung from his bones like tattered prison clothes. What hair remained was in tufts. His teeth had rotted. He smashed the mirror in his room. And he asked around, "Where is the old man?"

Within a week he arrived at the shanty.

He was carrying a wooden dowel under a heavy cloak and flexed his grip around the base, though he hoped not to use it. He had spent years dreaming of ways to kill the old fool. Most often he had fantasized about using his bare hands.

Smoke from the fire exited through the roof, and light flickered through holes in the wool blanket that covered the entrance. Rostek waited in the shadows and watched for movement in the surrounding homes. Assured no one could see, he moved through the darkness and came to the doorway. No sound came from within, and he crept closer, peering through a crack and waiting for his eyes to adjust. Nothing moved inside. If the old man was home he was sleeping.

Perfect.

Rostek's feet barely stirred the dirt as he gripped the stick and reached for the blanket with his other hand.

"Czerwinski."

A frail voice said his name from somewhere in the darkness, and he started. He let go of the blanket and spun around, pulling the rod from his coat and pointing it toward the voice.

His eyes adjusted again as he heard a woman clearing her throat.

A tiny figure emerged from the blackness. She was leaning on a cane and holding a small basket. She hobbled in his direction.

"It is Czerwinski, right?"

Rostek's body froze as he looked around to see who else was there.

The old woman mumbled as she came toward him, and at one point laughed at whomever she was talking to. She moved closer to the entrance, and Rostek, without thinking, stepped aside. She shoved her cane into the wool blanket and flooded the entryway with light.

Wrinkled eyes looked out from a tattered head cover as the lady leaned in within inches of Rostek's face and examined it, now awash in the firelight. He realized he was still holding the club out like a torch and felt foolish. He lowered it to his waist as the woman completed her inspection. Her eyes softened. "I wouldn't have recognized you," she said.

He continued to glance at the shadows, waiting for a trap to spring.

"Don't worry, son, I'm alone," she said.

"How do you—"

"Here, hold this," she said, and pushed the basket into his stomach. He took it on instinct as she pushed the blanket aside and bent over to enter the shanty.

"God told me months ago that you'd be coming," she said as she entered. "And when I saw you sneaking around I knew. Who else would be here acting like that?"

Holding the blanket aside, she made room. "Are you coming in?"

The gaunt man stared with his mouth open. He looked down at the basket—three radishes and half an onion.

The woman moved inside and let the blanket fall. "Suit yourself. But I'll need those veggies soon enough. I'll put the water on."

Rostek turned his back to the wall nearby and peered into the shadows. He had experienced fevers in the mines that brought hallucinations, but this was something new. This he could touch, and feel, and smell. This was real. The old woman was mocking him.

Who does she think she is?

Throwing the basket on the ground, he turned toward the blanket and yanked it aside. The dowel led the way as he entered.

"You listen to me, hag. How do you know my name?" He almost stumbled into the fire in his haste. The woman was shuffling toward him, straining under the weight of a large clay pot cradled in both hands. Unaffected, she crouched to place the pot on the rocks that edged the fire. Rostek pointed the stick in her direction.

When she was satisfied with the pot's position, she placed a hand on her lower back, groaned, and returned upright. Closing the few steps between the two, she touched the end of the rod and lowered it. Her eyes narrowed. "You dropped my radishes."

She exited the shanty, and Rostek could hear her grunting in the darkness as she retrieved her goods. He looked around the room as if someone there could help him.

Returning, the woman patted him on the back as she moved past. "The Mission gives me vegetables once a week," she said. "But it's okay, they'll clean up. Have a seat."

She moved back to the pot, where she crouched again and rubbed the vegetables with her dress.

The stick came back up. "Woman! Do you know who I am?! Do you ... Do you know what I could do to you?"

She didn't look up.

"You should keep your voice down, Rostek Czerwinski. If the neighbors hear ... and in your weakened state," she said as she dropped a piece of onion into the water. "And I know good and well who you are. And I know what you want."

"Where is the old man?" Czerwinski said and poked her in the shoulder with the stick. Sweat was beading on his forehead.

The old woman grimaced and looked at him. She touched her arm where he had jabbed her, and her expression was clear—*Why would you do something like that?*

Rostek kept the dowel pointed at her.

"Where is he?"

She stared into the man's face for several seconds. Her posture relaxed, and she sighed.

"I'm sorry to tell you this, but Dmitri is dead. Been gone five years." She motioned with her dull knife toward a wooden box in the corner near her sleeping mat. "He left something for you."

Rostek glanced at the box. "What are you playing at?! Stand up! Tell me where he is!" He reached for her and grabbed her dress at the shoulder. Clinching the fabric in one hand, he raised the club with the other.

Her head bowed as she waited for the blow. "Do what you came to do, but open the box."

Rostek shook her. "What are you trying to do? Tell me where he is or so help me–!" He held his position and waited for her response.

She wiped her nose with the back of her hand. It took a few moments for her to respond. When she did, her voice cracked. "Child, you killed my son ... and my husband. He died mourning that boy. What more could you take from me today?"

Looking at Rostek, tears filled her eyes as she pointed to the box. "We saved for a year to make that gift possible, son. I pledged to stay alive as long as I could. The least you could do is open it."

Rostek looked at the woman's wrinkled face and red eyes. "Just look," she said, "and then decide what to do."

He released his hold on her dress and lowered the stick. Wiping her hands, she scooted back to the pot and dabbed her eyes with her apron.

Rostek watched the woman stir the mixture for almost a minute before he looked back at the box. She was cleaning a bowl and appeared distracted, so he crossed the room, crouched, and opened the latch. He could hear her whispering, and he glanced over his shoulder. She was rocking back and forth with her eyes closed and lips moving. Pushing back the lid, he peered inside to see a small wooden cross. Attached to the cross was a rolled parchment held in place by a string.

The woman hadn't moved, and Rostek reached inside to remove the items. He loosened the string and unrolled the parchment.

Rostek Czerwinski,

I cannot write, but I have hired someone to transcribe this letter to you. I carved the cross and I hope you like it.

There has not been a day since my son died that I haven't prayed for you, and I prayed for months about your trial. I was unsure whether to prosecute or forgive and forget. I loved that boy more than life. Yet, you should know, I forgave you. I have hated every moment knowing you were rotting away and believed that somehow God would protect you and bring you back to us.

I believe God demanded your trial, though I might have chosen otherwise. He has a message for you, and it could only be received after your imprisonment.

Just as you have suffered in jail, surrounded by terror, sickness, and pain with no hope of escape—that is the suffering you have put hundreds through in your houses of prostitution, alcohol, and gambling. And just as you have come to hold me accountable for your imprisonment, those poor souls you have bound will stand at the judgment and speak at your trial before God. He has heard their pleas.

But it is not too late, my friend. Remember what my boy told you. God loves the abuser as well as the abused.

You are one whom God can use to set captives free.

My wife can tell you more of the Savior. I beg of you, listen to her.

With all my heart, I love you. I wish I could have helped you in your pain.

Dmitri

"Child, how about we have some soup?" The woman's soft voice came from behind him.

Rostek left the tent without conversation. He threw the cross in the fire and cussed at the woman. For the next few days she prayed.

He had taken the letter with him.

Four days later she was sitting by the fire when a hushed voice came from outside.

"Ma'am."

"Yes, Rostek. Come in, son."

Six months later, Rostek stood on a crate in the middle of the Grease. His chest was moving in and out, and his legs threatened to give way. Whispering a quiet prayer, he summoned his courage, leaned his head back, and shouted as loud as he could.

"I ONCE KILLED A MAN RIGHT HERE IN THE GREASE!"

Years later the Grease was a memory. A church stood in the spot where Mieszko and Rostek had preached.

It began with an adoption. It moved through a boy willing to risk everything, and it continued through a woman loving and brave enough to make soup for an enemy.

It shows how the Kingdom has always moved.

What part will you have played when all history is revealed, my friend?

Seek God in solitude, pray, love His Word, and walk unashamed. It always will end in a life that changes the world.

Aulus

LETTER FOURTEEN
The View From Here

Precious One,

You should see my office here.

I will do my best to describe it in your language. Words relating time, distance, or color fall short. When you say "beautiful" you mean pleasing to the sight or other senses. Here, we have hundreds of words for beautiful. It goes beyond the sensual and stretches to the soul. It is pleasure that builds until we can't take any more, and then, through faith, our capacity increases.

Trying to tell you about Heaven is like a three-dimensional being describing his world to a two-dimensional man. It can't be done. How much more for one who flows among dozens of dimensions? In previous descriptions I down-played this and described Heaven in your terms. I will continue to do so, but be aware that the medium of our communication prohibits clarity.

My work desk in Heaven varies in size by my mood and other factors. Sometimes it is intimate and crafted of materials you would view as "antique"—deep mahogany woods with inlaid marble and granite. At other times it's unrestrained and powerful, like a battleship blasting through oceans.

And the view? Beyond breathtaking.

My home is a mansion that makes mansions in your world seem like shacks.

I have been assigned Governor over one area of the Kingdom, and I live on the side of a mountain overlooking this area. Visualize razor-edged mountain crests that go on for miles at 50,000 feet, and you may understand. My office suite jets out on the side of one crest and spans half a mile before it couples with another mountain—the ultimate room with a view.

There are no roads or other mechanical means of coming to my home, but movement is different here and, like everything else, accomplished through faith. Having ever-increasing faith since arriving, I can move from one location in my home to another in the cities below as easily as you can move across a room.

I have dozens of decks that line the expanse of my office suite. Some are for praying, some are for entertaining, and still others are for training or mentoring. As I pen this letter, I am on my writing deck in what you might describe as a hammock, and my desk is stretched before me.

To my left is a railing, and far below the rail are expansive cities that run through deep valleys of purple and green.

Over the horizon is the Light of God. Though there are planets and stars here, they come and go by different rules, and illumination does not depend on them. Instead, God expresses Himself through light. For one period of time the air is filled with bursting orange hues with yellow trim. And later, deep magentas and shimmering blues. Imagine a clear, star-filled night with crickets chirping and the smell of honeysuckle hanging in the air, and you will know one thousandth of the serene calm of those times.

And that is the mood at this moment—a mood highlighted by fine music rolling in with the breeze. It is a tune from one of Heaven's most promising music students, and for a moment I allow my thoughts to drift to his classroom. The boy is seated at an instrument you wouldn't recognize with one of Earth's greatest composers standing behind him, one hand resting on the young man's shoulder. And God is flowing between the two. When the boy reaches the last few notes, he looks at his beaming instructor, who speaks. "As I've always said, my boy, there is nothing difficult about it. Play the right notes at the right time, and the instrument does the rest."

The next song takes off at a frenzied pace, and a golden light dissolves across the sky, warming the area and the valley below. I hear an immense crowd cheer in one of the stadiums. I am not sure what has caused the eruption, but I feel their joy and celebrate with them.

I tell you this to show you the harmony here. The atmosphere ebbs and flows with the glory of God according to His will. And all in the Kingdom are in touch. We have celebrations that might last months, followed by retreats of stillness that stretch for years. The air will be filled with singing one day and silence the next. As we live here, we become more and more in tune with the side of God He reveals at any given time. On the explosive, brilliant days I'm often throwing a party, with hundreds or even thousands attending. And in the cooler, still times, I am curled up with a book or seeking God's face in whispered tones with a small group of friends. Some of those friends I will have known for years, and others I might have met that day.

In a circle like that might be a former scholar who will lend logic and reason to the gathering. Another might be a former laborer who has developed a depth of thought beyond the scholar, but humbles himself and lets the scholar talk. Yet another is a woman who makes incredible food and enjoys watching it consumed. And she is the smartest of the three.

Each relationship here is so full of the Life of God that the best relationships on Earth cannot compare. Here we connect on levels that surpass any amount of intimacy you have known. Think

H.L. HUSSMANN

of being in love, with all the spinning emotions involved—when one look or one touch from your beloved fills your chest with warmth. Even the casual acquaintance here carries more depth and more feeling. I am in love with every person. Heaven is the consummate "in love" experience. There is never a moment when I don't feel I could burst from the love and joy that fills me.

My dear friend, I feel the same toward you. I can hardly wait to meet you in person. That one moment will be such a joy that you would sacrifice anything—wealth, sex, time, or effort—to attain it. And it will pale to meeting Jesus, the source of all joy and the Captain of your salvation.

As I write today, there is a friend nearby. He is replacing a set of bookcases on my writing deck with a new design of his own.

When he is finished, I will have access to writings and teachings produced far from here. With just a thought, the books I desire will be shelved. I will be able to peruse, but more than that, I will contribute. He will build three dozen others, and I will join a collective with their owners. Through those books, we will share knowledge with one another—and the tool for doing so will be this man's brilliant design created for only a handful of people.

But why am I one of them?

The man, Mateio, was raised on a small island in the South Pacific and lived hundreds of years after me. What could qualify me for such a gift?

Seventeen hundred years before Mateio was born I shared the Gospel with an individual and set in motion a course of history. Generations went by, and one day, when Mateio was in his mid-twenties, he listened to a missionary who emerged from that lineage of faith. Mateio embraced Jesus. For some time in Heaven he has tracked down his spiritual heritage and desires to reward several of those who contributed. I am the latest he has tracked down.

When the bookcase is complete, we will lounge together and play a game of "what if." I will pretend he lived generations before I did and that our roles were reversed. In this scenario it was he who contributed to my salvation. And I will reward him in a way I see fit—not because it is true, but because it is fun. I will give to him what such a man deserves, which is much.

I could fill books full of letters describing the people I have met here who have descended from what I considered insignificant acts on Earth:

- I gave a small financial gift toward building a church. A thousand years later, tens of thousands were following Jesus.

- I preached a sermon—a poor one, but a seed was planted in one individual. Fourteen hundred years later, hope and relief were offered to hundreds of orphans.

- I shared hope with a stranger, and today, though I understand if it is difficult to believe, tens of millions have heard the Gospel. Hundreds of thousands have responded. Hospitals have been built, and universities have been established. Governments and nations have been shaped.

Do you see, over time, the impact of serving Jesus every moment?

There is nothing like spending time with Mateio and reflecting on what God has done. When I shared the message of Jesus with a stranger almost two millennia before Mateio was born, I was uncomfortable. I never considered that one day it would lead to a friend for all eternity. Every time we see each other it is a reunion of brothers, and sooner than you imagine it will be the same with you and me.

I can't explain how much I look forward to the day we share a meal together and marvel at what God has done.

My closing thought is a prayer–that Heaven will be filled with those you have touched.

May you bring them with you.

Aulus

H.L. HUSSMANN

Discussion Questions
Letter One - The Story of Aulus Aurelius

- Read Mark 8:34-35. What does this passage mean to you? In practice, what would it look like to follow this teaching?

- Most of us will never literally give our lives for the Gospel, but what are some ways we can still "take up our cross" and follow in the footsteps of Jesus?

- Aulus was faced with the terrible decision of saving his family or refusing to deny Jesus. Read Luke 14:25-33 and 1 Corinthians 7:29-21. What do these passages say about God's view on what our highest priorities should be?

- Aulus' "moment of truth" came after years of following Jesus. What do you suspect his life looked like in daily terms? What habits, thoughts, or practices do you imagine prepared him for that moment? How are those different from the ones in your own life?

Discussion Questions
Letter Two - A Journey to Real Life

- When you think of Heaven, what is it like? Do people eat? Play musical instruments? Have pets? Read Revelation 21:1-5 and 22:1-5. How do these descriptions compare to your view?

- Do you believe we will continue to study and learn in Heaven? Why or why not?

- In this letter, Tian Wei describes joy as a "commodity" in Heaven. What did you think about that? How could that apply to your life?

- Read 1 John 2:17. The Bible teaches that this life will one day be obsolete but that what happens in this life determines, to an extent, what the next will be like. How do you believe this life affects the next?

Discussion Questions
Letter Three - A Shared Trait of Heaven

- In the Lord's Prayer, Jesus says we should pray that God's will is done on Earth as it is in Heaven. If Heaven is similar to what this letter describes, what does that mean for Earth? Elaborate.

- In this letter, Aulus says, "The line of people entering Heaven is always a line of broken people. But more, it's a line of broken people who know they are broken. They have no delusions of qualifying on their own." What do you think about that?

- Aulus also says that "self-confidence, apart from God, is the road to Hell." Luke 18:9-14 seems to agree. What are your thoughts on this passage?

- This letter speaks about humility. How do you define humility? How can a person become humble?

Discussion Questions
Letter Four - Choosing to Choose

* What thoughts did this letter bring up? Read Genesis 3:1-24. How was Aulus' story different than you've imagined it before?

* In this letter and in the Biblical narrative, the serpent asks, "Did God really say ...?" What are some variations of that question that still confront Christians today? How should a Christian respond?

* Aulus mentions that before the fall, humanity was capable of walking in God's presence and being intimate with Him. Is that still possible? If so, how? Read 2 Corinthians 5:17-20.

* This letter brings up the topic of "Who's in charge here?" Do you believe that is an important question today? Why or why not?

* Aulus concludes his letter with, "'Freedom' is often bondage in disguise." What do you think he meant?

Discussion Questions
Letter Five - The Beauty that Destroys

- How was Kate deceived? How might her story relate to our lives?

- Aulus says the enemy "makes the hideous seem attractive and the vacant seem full." What do you think this means? What are some examples of this idea?

- Read 2 Corinthians 11:14. What are some areas of your own life that seem good to you but might not be?

- Aulus mentions that every part of you that is not filled with God is filled with the "nothing" of the world. What does it look like to be filled with God? How can that be achieved?

- 1 Peter 1:3-9 mentions that through faith we can be "shielded" by God's power. What do you think that means?

Discussion Questions
Letter Six - The Heart of the Matter

* Do you agree with Aulus that pain related to relationships is the most terrible kind of pain? Why or why not?

* Aulus says, "At the center of your life is the need for connection." What do you think about that?

* Read John 3:16 and John 17:3. What do these passages say about our relational connection with God?

* Savannah shows up at Sharri's door at precisely the right time. Do you think God desires we do the same in other people's lives? How can we?

* Aulus closes this letter with, "His business is healing people." Do you believe that? What is an example you've seen of God doing this?

- Aulus speaks of solitude and stillness as essential needs in a believer's life. Do you agree? Why or why not?

- The poet Walter Savage Landor said, "Solitude is the audience chamber of God." Have you ever experienced God's presence in solitude? Elaborate.

- Aulus mentions lives filled with distraction and a "vulgar pursuit of diversion." What are your thoughts on this? Are there areas of your life in which this rings true? What can you do about it?

- Aulus describes situations in which his wife seems to be more in tune with God by seeking Him in silence. Do you believe that is possible? Why or why not?

- Read Luke 5:15-16, 6:12-13, and Matthew 14:10-13 and 23. What do these passages tell us of Jesus' view on solitude?

Discussion Questions
Letter Eight - The Word is Life

* Describe your personal view on the value of the Bible by first describing what it is in reality. Compare that to what you believe it *should* be. How can you make the former the latter?

* Do you believe you have a good grasp on how the original words of the Bible were passed down to Christians today? How could you learn more about this topic?

* Would you risk your life for access to the Bible? Why or why not?

* Hien Pham received encouragement from the Bible at the right time in the right place. Have you ever had a similar experience? Elaborate.

* Read John 6:60-69. Simon Peter refuses to abandon Jesus, saying he recognizes that Jesus has the "words of eternal life." What do you think that means? How does that relate to the value we place on the Bible?

Discussion Questions
Letter Nine - Sending and Receiving

- What are some difficulties you encounter where prayer is concerned? Did this letter offer any insight?

- Read Ecclesiastes 5:1-2 and Matthew 6:7. What do these verses teach about prayer?

- Do you think about communication with God as a back-and-forth process? Why or why not? How can we become more adept at receiving from God through prayer?

- Aulus says if you admit your dependence on God where prayer is concerned, He will prove you right but fill your need. What do you think about this?

- Aulus also mentions that your only part in this process is availability. What do you think he meant by that? Do you agree? Why or why not?

Discussion Questions
Letter Ten - The Parable of the Well

• What did you get out of this letter? What do you think the parable meant?

• If life is related to this parable, what is the goal of the "challenge"? How can the goal be reached?

• It is implied there is a big difference between just making it through the challenge and conquering it. What are your thoughts on this? How does this relate to your life?

• Talk about the king in the parable. How is he like God? How is he different?

• Read John 7:37-38. In this passage, Jesus stood up in front of a huge crowd at the end of an important religious festival to announce these words in public. Describe your response to His declaration. Describe other responses that might have come from the crowd.

Discussion Questions
Letter Eleven - Saved From the Cold

* Read Luke 4:14-20, another public proclamation by Jesus. What does it say about Jesus' ministry to the poor, to prisoners, and to the oppressed? What does it mean to us today?

* Read Mark 12:41-44. What does this lesson of Jesus say to how much of our lives should be given to God? How does this relate to your own life?

* Read James 1:27. Talk about your reaction to this verse.

* Talk about a time someone sacrificed for you. Did you desire the help? How does this relate to the Golden Rule of Jesus to "do unto others as you would have them do unto you?" Do you believe in the concept of "paying it forward"?

* Aulus says, "You cannot help everyone. But you can rescue some." Do you agree? Why or why not?

- Aulus asks, "Did the boy fail?" What do you think? Did he? Why or why not?

- Read Acts 6:8-15 and 7:51-60. What are your thoughts on Stephen's proclamation? Did he do anything wrong? Elaborate.

- Read Matthew 10 with an emphasis on verses 13, 14, 19, 20, and 26-31. What does this passage emphasize as far as Jesus is concerned? In the spectrum between confident boldness and fear, where does Jesus seem to indicate the believer should be?

- Mieszko says that Jesus Christ loves the abuser as much as He does the abused. What do you think about that?

- Throughout history Christians have died for proclaiming the Gospel of Jesus, but many others have failed to proclaim due to fear. What fears do you believe hold Christians back? How can we conquer those fears?

Discussion Questions
Letter Thirteen - Redemption

- What did you get out of this letter?

- Do you believe every life influences others and that history unfolds through the small daily activities of men? How can your actions today shape the future?

- Could you have the boldness of the old woman in the face of potential violence? What is the right response to such a situation?

- Read Matthew 5:43-48. What does this passage tell us about our attitude toward people who have hurt us? How can we acquire that attitude?

- Aulus says, "Seek God in solitude, pray, love His Word, and walk unashamed. It will always end in a life that changes the world." Do you agree? Why or why not?

- Identify a time you felt serene. What, in particular, allowed such a feeling?

- Do you believe some in Heaven will be rewarded more than others? Why or why not? Read Matthew 25:14-28, 1 Corinthians 3:13-15, and Revelation 22:12.

- Aulus describes a unity of mind in Heaven. Should there be a similar phenomenon among believers on Earth? Why or why not? If yes, how can that be pursued?

- Aulus closes with "My closing prayer for you is that Heaven will be filled with those you have touched." What does that mean to you?

- What concluding thoughts do you have concerning *Letters From a Martyred Christian*? What practical steps will you take as a result of reading Aulus' letters?

USMISSIONS.AG.ORG

WE are THERE THAT NONE PERISH

Chaplaincy Ministries **1**

Chi Alpha Campus Ministries, U.S.A. **2**

Intercultural Ministries **3**

Missionary Church Planters & Developers **4**

Teen Challenge International, U.S.A. **5**

U.S. MAPS **6**

Youth Alive **7**

U.S. MISSIONS
...that none perish

USMISSIONS.AG.ORG

U.S. MISSIONS
we are there
...that none perish
U.S. Missions reached a milestone in 2012: seventy-five years of taking the gospel to those who are hurting and perishing in the United States!
ASSEMBLIES OF GOD U.S. MISSIONS
75
75TH ANNIVERSARY
U.S. MISSIONS
...that none perish
usmissions.ag.org

CHI ALPHA EXPEDITIONS

Every Student Goes
Every Student Gives
Every Student Prays
Every Student Welcomes

Did you enjoy LFMC? **Please consider writing a review on Amazon.com.**

Purchase multiple copies for use in Bible studies and small groups - LettersFromAMartyr.com

TRAIN YOUR CONGREGATION OR CONFERENCE ATTENDEES: H.L. Hussmann is available for speaking engagements or consultation.

Overcoming Fear • Loving God With Passion • Who Was Jesus? Dialoguing With Atheists • Other Religions • Consistency in Outreach • Church Growth • Missions
HLHussmann.com